Medical Staff
Credentialing
A PRACTICAL GUIDE

Fay A. Rozovsky, J.D., Lorne E. Rozovsky, LL.B., and Linda M. Harpster, J.D.

81167

AHA books are published by American Hospital Publishing, Inc., an American Hospital Association company

This publication is designed to provide accurate and authoritative information in regard to the subject matter covered. It is sold with the understanding that the publisher and the authors are not engaged in rendering legal, accounting, or other professional services. If legal advice or other expert assistance is required, the services of a competent professional should be sought.

The views expressed in this publication are strictly those of the authors and do not necessarily represent official positions of the American Hospital Association.

Library of Congress Cataloging-in-Publication Data

Rozovsky, F. A. (Fay Adrienne), 1950–
   Medical staff credentialing : a practical guide / Fay A. Rozovsky,
Lorne E. Rozovsky, and Linda M. Harpster.
      p.   cm.
   Includes bibliographical references
   ISBN 1-55648-112-8 (pbk.)
   1. Hospitals—Medical staff—Clinical privileges. 2. Hospitals—
Medical staff—Selection and appointment. 3. Hospitals—Medical
staff—Rating of. 4. Hospitals—Medical staff—Discipline.
I. Rozovsky, Lorne Elkin. II. Harpster, Linda Marie. III. Title.
   [DNLM: 1. Credentialing. 2. Medical Staff, Hospital—organization
& administration. 3. Personnel Administration, Hospital—
organization & administration. WX 159 R893m 1993]
RA972.R694 1993
362.1'1'0683—dc20
DNLM/DLC
for Library of Congress   93-33354
                                                                                CIP

Catalog no. 145102

©1994 by American Hospital Publishing, Inc.,
an American Hospital Association company

Printed in the USA

ΑΗΑ is a service mark of the American Hospital Association used under license by American Hospital Publishing, Inc.

Text set in Trump
3M—12/93—0361

Audrey Kaufman, Acquisitions/Development Editor
Anne Hermann, Production Editor
Peggy DuMais, Production Coordinator
Luke Smith, Cover Designer
Marcia Bottoms, Books Division Assistant Director
Brian Schenk, Books Division Director

Contents

List of Figures

About the Authors

Fay A. Rozovsksy, J.D., M.P.H., DASHRM, is the associate director for risk management of the Franciscan Health System based in Aston, Pennsylvania. A member of the Massachusetts and Florida Bars, she received a master's degree in public health from Harvard. Mrs. Rozovsky has served as a consultant to health care facilities in the United States and Canada. She has authored several books and articles on consent to treatment, health care record keeping, and related issues. In 1992, she was named a Diplomat by the American Society for Healthcare Risk Management.

Lorne E. Rozovsky, LL.B., Q.C., is a vice-president of LEFAR Health Associates, Inc., an international health management firm specializing in risk management consulting and education. He advises health professionals, associations, and institutions, and for many years was adjunct associate professor of law and medicine at Dalhousie University. He is the author of 11 books and over 500 articles and is editor of *RRM Report*, a risk management reporter published by LEFAR Health Associates, Inc. He has lectured widely in the United States, Canada, Europe, Africa, the West Indies, and Israel. In 1984, Mr. Rozovsky was appointed Queen's Counsel, and, in 1986, he was made an Honorary Fellow of the American College of Legal Medicine.

Linda Marie Harpster, J.D., is associate general counsel, health affairs, for the University of Cincinnati. She received her J.D. from Chase College of Law in 1978. Prior to the position she now holds, Ms. Harpster was vice-president and general counsel for Lutheran Hospital of Indiana and before that served as director of legal services for Sisters of Charity Health Care Systems, headquartered in Cincinnati. She began her career as a risk manager for St. Francis-St. George Hospital, also located in Cincinnati. Ms. Harpster is a frequent speaker and author and serves on the editorial board of *Health Law Week*. She is the coeditor of *Risk Management Handbook for Health Care Facilities* (Chicago: American Hospital Publishing, 1990).

Acknowledgments

This book is based in large measure on the experience of many people, including that of the authors. To all of those people in hospitals across the country who have struggled for years to develop a system of marrying doctors to hospitals, we are extremely indebted.

We also wish to thank two research assistants, Nina Edwards and Robert Blaisdell, students at Boston University School of Law, for their careful and methodical research; and Juanita Swinamer of LEFAR Health Associates, Inc., for her administrative skills and encouragement. And we extend thanks to Audrey Kaufman of American Hospital Publishing, Inc., whose patience and kindness got us through a most challenging project.

Introduction

Hospitals have come a long way from being places of last resort for the poor and the dying to highly sophisticated institutions dedicated to the treatment and cure of the ill and injured. Years ago, the law viewed hospital caregivers in much the same way that it viewed innkeepers. Today, the law recognizes that hospitals have developed along a very different path from hotels. The innkeeper analogy no longer fits.

Traditionally, the law and society looked on the hospital as exercising little, if any, control over the actions of staff physicians. Because staff physicians were seen as independent contractors who borrowed the services of allied health care personnel, the law was quite lenient when it came to holding hospitals accountable for the negligence of those physicians who injured patients while treating them on the premises of the health care facility.

In time, the old hands-off approach fell to the wayside and hospitals began to exert considerable power over who could admit and treat patients. The impetus for this change in the contemporary approach to medical staff credentialing cannot be ascribed to a single source; rather, it was influenced by a number of factors.

Earlier this century, concerns about the quality of care provided by physicians led Dr. Codman, a Boston-area physician, to issue a challenge to his colleagues. It was a challenge for better education, peer training and monitoring, and improved patient care. To some extent, the antecedents to contemporary credentialing can be linked to Dr. Codman's insistence on better-quality medical practice.

However, today many other factors have converged to formulate the credentialing process. The advent of hospital accreditation, judicial pronouncements on due process, financial incentives from agencies controlling reimbursement, and litigation alleging substandard care have all influenced the scope and shape of the mandate for medical staff credentialing. An array of federal and state legislative and regulatory requirements regarding reimbursement, antitrust, quality improvement initiatives at the hospital level, clinical practice parameters, and treatment outcomes have intensified the pressure.

Although concerns about the quality of care are a driving force behind contemporary credentialing efforts, it is the law that is providing the greatest impetus for change. The regulatory requirements are extensive, as is the risk of litigation for negligent credentialing of staff physicians.

However, hospitals are getting mixed messages in this regard. At the same time that they are admonished to provide high-quality care in a cost-effective manner and to scrutinize the qualifications of physicians who seek privileges, they are constrained by federal and state laws that assure doctors of due process, human rights, and civil rights.

In the face of these challenges, hospitals have a mandate to credential members of the medical staff properly. In order to do so, they must take into account what is right for the patients, the community, the physicians, and the institutions themselves. Additionally, they need to develop a practical approach to credentialing, which means being flexible and avoiding reliance on immutable assumptions. A practical approach to credentialing requires communication and participation, not an adverserial attitude between hospitals and physicians. It is indeed different from approaches used in the past, but it is an approach that promises to keep all involved in the process challenged in their efforts to credential members of the medical staff.

A practical approach to credentialing requires addressing certain fundamental questions:

- What information is needed in order to credential members of the medical staff?
- How can hospitals obtain the details needed in a cost-effective and efficient manner?
- How can hospitals gain the cooperation of the medical staff in this process?
- How can hospitals avoid clashes with the medical staff?
- How can hospitals avoid problems under federal and state regulatory requirements that present roadblocks to obtaining important credentialing information?
- How can hospitals insulate themselves from allegations of negligent credentialing?

Unfortunately, there is no magic formula for credentialing physicians in an expeditious and cost-effective manner. What works for a rural hospital may not work for an urban hospital. The bottom line is that hospitals have to develop an approach to credentialing that works for them.

Development of an effective and yet practical credentialing system is not the sole responsibility of the medical director or the medical staff; hospital administration also should have input. In addition, the input of legal counsel should be sought to help avoid many of the legal impediments that can preclude development of an effective credentialing system. It is critical to avoid turf battles. In essence, the key is to take a consensus-building approach that works for everyone.

Once in place, the credentialing system should not be treated as if it were cast in stone. Like other elements of hospital management, it should be reviewed and upgraded periodically. With the impending changes promised under national health care reform, the need to be flexible in developing and using a medical credentialing system will be greater than ever.

Most hospitals are still at the early stages of quality improvement initiatives. Many are learning about the development and use of practice guidelines and clinical practice parameters. Using this information in the credentialing process will affect physician practices and will help determine who is recommended for staff privileges.

This book is designed for people who manage or in some way direct the relationship between hospitals and physicians. At one time, the medical staff organization and the hospital were separate entities. Today, they are closely interwoven. Therefore, credentialing is of interest to medical directors, presidents of medical staffs, members of credentials committees, and members of medical executive committees. On the hospital side, members of the board, chief executive officers (CEOs) and their senior staff members who either are involved in delivering health care in the hospital or are affected by staff physicians will all have an interest in this subject. Thus, this book offers basic education for everyone involved in or with medical staff. It focuses on understanding the basic practical problems of determining whether, and to what extent, a physician will be permitted to practice within the hospital.

In addition, *Medical Staff Credentialing: A Practical Guide* is a sourcebook for assistance in dealing with specific problems. However, when referring to this book for assistance, readers must remember that it is *not* a substitute for obtaining legal advice. Advice from a lawyer is tailored to specific circumstances, whereas a book offers general principles and helps readers adapt advice to circumstances they may encounter in their own institutions.

This book also is designed to be used by lawyers, although it neither discusses the law in depth nor provides full case citations. However, it does bring into focus many of the legal problems or legal implications that are likely to arise in the credentialing process. This book should help lawyers identify problems more clearly so that they can provide individualized advice to clients. For a discussion of specific legal subjects, reference should be made to texts on such matters.

This book is divided into two parts, Introduction and Overview (chapters 1 through 4) and Implementation of the Process (chapters 5 through 9). In the first part, chapter 1 discusses the legal and agency requirements that apply to medical staff credentialing and identifies who must be credentialed. Chapter 2 considers the legal issues of due process and incorporating the concept of fairness in the process of taking an action against a physician's privileges. Chapter 3 identifies the key participants in the credentialing process and describes their roles and responsibilities. Chapter 4 provides an overview of the credentialing process. In the second part of the book, chapter 5 discusses the procedure involved in the initial appointment for privileges. Chapter 6 continues the discussion as it applies to the procedure for reappointment to the medical staff. Chapter 7 examines the requirements in legislation, rules and regulations, and hospital bylaws that provide a framework for suspending, restricting, or revoking privileges. Chapter 8 explains the concept of economic credentialing and deals with other issues and trends that are beginning to have an impact on the credentialing process. Finally, chapter 9 looks at credentialing issues for small and rural hospitals.

Introduction
and Overview

1 | Background Issues

Introduction

The modern hospital, regardless of its size, is amazingly complex. A range of medical specialists and specialized allied health professionals use extremely sophisticated and highly technological equipment to diagnose and treat illness. For the most part, the public is unaware of this complexity and of the difficulty of bringing all the specialists together to coordinate the care of a single patient. Patients simply assume that, for their stay in the hospital, their physicians and the hospital's nurses and technicians are competent, skilled, and dedicated. Courts, governments, and accrediting organizations regulate health care organizations in an attempt to provide patients the assurance they want that the health care system will take good care of them. The patient's trust, backed by the force of law, provides the impetus for hospitals to become ever more conscientious in examining the skills and the professionalism of their employees and of the physicians who use hospital resources to take care of their patients.

This chapter discusses the various legal and agency requirements that apply to medical staff credentialing. In addition, it introduces discussion of who must be credentialed and the legal options available to physicians who want to contest a hospital's adverse credentialing action.

Common Law

The body of case law that has developed since 1965 from what is considered the seminal case, *Darling v. Charleston Community Memorial Hospital*,[1] makes it clear that courts will hold the hospital responsible for both the safe nursing care of the patient and monitoring the quality of physicians' practices in the hospital. In the *Darling* case, Dr. Alexander, a physician on the hospital's staff who was covering the hospital's emergency department, treated 18-year-old Dorrence Darling for a broken leg. The patient's leg eventually had to be amputated when gangrene developed because the cast applied by Dr. Alexander restricted blood circulation in the leg. The patient sued the hospital claiming, among other things, that the hospital should have known that she was not recovering and should have required Dr. Alexander to consult with another physician. It was in this case that the Illinois Supreme Court expressly eliminated charitable immunity as a defense for hospitals sued for negligence.[2] The court also expressly rejected the notion that the hospital's function is merely "to procure [doctors and nurses] to act upon their own responsibility."[3] The court stated that:

[T]he Standards for Hospital Accreditation, the state licensing regulations and the defendant's bylaws demonstrate that the medical profession and other responsible authorities regard it as both desirable and feasible that a hospital assume certain responsibilities for the care of the patient.[4]

A more recent case expressly imposed on the hospital a legal duty to credential physicians. Dr. Salinsky was chief of staff at Misericordia Hospital and performed orthopedic surgery there. He and the hospital were sued by a patient who suffered injury when Dr. Salinsky attempted to remove a pin fragment from the patient's right hip.[5] The patient's claim against the hospital was that the hospital knew or should have known that Dr. Salinsky was not competent to perform the procedure and that it failed to investigate Dr. Salinsky's qualifications.

The evidence showed that the hospital did not investigate the information that Dr. Salinsky had provided in his application for appointment and privileges. Had the hospital done so, it would have discovered that Dr. Salinsky falsified most of the information. Further evidence showed that 10 malpractice suits were pending against Dr. Salinsky; that, contrary to his assertions, his orthopedic surgery privileges had been terminated at several hospitals; and that he had signed the approval form for privileges. His application was never formally acted on by either the medical executive committee or the board of trustees.

One of the arguments the hospital made in its defense was that the plaintiff was required to show that the physician was incompetent and that the plaintiff should have made the hospital aware of that incompetence. However, the Wisconsin Supreme Court stated that, in its opinion, the plaintiff only had to prove that the hospital did not make a reasonable effort to find out whether Dr. Salinsky was qualified.[6] The court went on to say that hospitals have a legal duty under the common law to "perform a thorough evaluation of medical staff applicants from the standpoint of professional competence, ethics, established reputation, and further, to periodically review the qualifications of its staff through a peer review or medical audit mechanism."[7]

The hospital's duty to monitor the practices of physicians on its staff was further defined in *Elam v. College Park Hospital*.[8] In this case, the patient, Sophie Elam, sued her podiatric surgeon for malpractice and also sued College Park Hospital where the surgery was performed, claiming that the hospital owed a legal duty to her to exercise reasonable care in selecting and reviewing the competency of physicians on its medical staff. Part of the evidence presented was the hospital's admission that it was aware of medical malpractice suits filed against the physician but that it did not consider the suits in credentialing the podiatrist. The court agreed that the hospital did indeed have such a duty. As previous courts had done, it relied on state statutes and accreditation standards that require investigation of a physician's competency for initial appointment and periodic review of competency before reappointment.

The failure of the hospital to fulfill its duty to use reasonable efforts to review the competency of staff physicians is called *corporate negligence*. The court noted that "the community hospital has evolved into a corporate institution" and that imposing this duty upon the hospital will provide it with a "greater incentive to assure the competence of its medical staff and the quality of medical care rendered within its walls."[9]

State Statutes

Hospitals are subject to the hospital licensing laws of the state in which they do business. For example, Ohio requires that, in order to operate, a hospital within the state must be certified under Title XVIII of the Social Security Act (42 U.S.C. 301), or be accredited by the Joint Commission on Accreditation of Health Care Organizations (JCAHO) or by the American Osteopathic Association.[10] Hospitals must provide proof to the Ohio Department of Health of their certification or accreditation in a timely fashion. Hospitals that do not do so shall be closed.[11] Because the JCAHO requires the hospital to have a credentialing procedure in place for accreditation, a hospital that chooses to submit its accreditation status in order to be licensed will be demonstrating that it meets criteria for credentialing.

Ohio statutes also require that a physician, dentist, or osteopath who admits a patient, or a podiatrist who coadmits a patient, be a member of the hospital's medical staff. All the hospital's patients must be under the medical supervision of a doctor of medicine or osteopathy, except that a dentist may admit solely for the purpose of providing dental services.

Ohio further requires that the governing body of every hospital set standards and procedures for considering and acting upon applications for staff membership or professional privileges. These standards must be made available to the public upon request.[12] The statute does not speak directly to credentialing, but case law decided under these statutes gives hospitals broad discretion in determining who shall be permitted to have staff privileges without interference by the courts.[13] It also imposes a duty to use reasonable care in selecting and granting privileges to physicians or risk liability to an injured plaintiff.[14]

Each state's statutory requirements regarding medical staff membership, physicians' admitting privileges, and the peer review and credentialing process will be somewhat different. The hospital must make its medical staff aware of what state statutes require as well as of what the common law regards as the duty of the hospital to monitor the care of patients in the facility.

Federal Requirements

In order to receive Medicare reimbursement, hospitals must comply with standards established in the Medicare regulations, called the *Conditions of Participation*. As many states do, Medicare relies on accreditation by the JCAHO to determine whether a hospital is in compliance with the Conditions of Participation. This reliance is called giving the hospital *deemed status*. However, if Medicare determines that a JCAHO-accredited hospital does not meet the Conditions of Participation, it may do its own survey for Medicare reimbursement.

The Conditions of Participation require that the hospital have an organized medical staff that is responsible to the governing body and operates under written bylaws. The governing body must make certain that the medical staff is accountable to it for the quality of patient care. Under the Conditions of Participation, the governing body must establish criteria for the selection of members of the medical staff, and appointees to the staff must have the appropriate character, competence, training, experience, and judgment. The medical staff must periodically conduct appraisals of its members. Compliance with the Conditions of Participation also is required for Medicaid reimbursement.

The Joint Commission on Accreditation of Healthcare Organizations

The JCAHO requires that every independent practitioner who provides patient services within the hospital must be credentialed to do so. This requirement applies whether or not the practitioner is a member of the medical staff. The medical staff of the hospital must be organized, the JCAHO says, and must be responsible to the governing board for the quality of care provided. The mechanism required by the JCAHO for credentialing physicians places ultimate responsibility on the governing body, which must act on recommendations from the medical staff concerning medical staff appointment, reappointments, terminations of appointments, and grants or revisions of clinical privileges.

The medical staff must adopt bylaws that will, among other things, provide for self-governance and accountability to the governing body. The bylaws must specify the mechanism by which privileges are granted. Not all hospitals seek JCAHO accreditation, but courts as well as state and federal legislators look to JCAHO standards as an important guide to set minimum hospital standards for monitoring the quality of care provided to patients by staff physicians. Hospital administrators must be aware of all these sources of regulations on medical staff performance.

The Health Care Quality Improvement Act

The most recent congressional effort to set standards for hospitals to follow when credentialing the medical staff is the Health Care Quality Improvement Act (HCQIA).[15] It was enacted by Congress in 1986 to encourage health care entities to closely monitor physician practice in the hospital by providing immunity from liability for credentialing and privileging. Immunity is available to peer review committees and the people who are members of, or staff to, the committees; people who provide information to the committees; and people who are under contract with the professional review body to conduct or assist with the professional review process. If the hospital provides minimum due process, as specified in the statute, prior to taking an action that adversely affects a physician's ability to practice in the hospital, the immunity applies. Congress believed that if physicians and hospitals were not afraid of the liability for taking adverse actions, they would be more likely to engage in vigorous peer review.

The second part of the HCQIA provides a means for hospitals to get information about physicians and dentists who are applying for appointment or reappointment. The information is compiled by the National Practitioner Data Bank. Actions taken by health care entities to terminate, reduce, suspend, or limit physicians' privileges for longer than 30 days for reasons of clinical competence or professional conduct must be reported to state medical boards. State medical boards receive this information and transmit it to the data bank. In addition, state licensing boards and professional societies must report actions adverse to physicians' licenses or other professional review actions to the National Practitioner Data Bank.

The act also requires reporting malpractice payments to the data bank. Insurance companies, self-insured practitioners, hospitals, and professional associations must report all payments made on behalf of a physician or dentist in settlement of, or in satisfaction of, a judgment or claim against the practitioner for the provision of health care services.

The act states that it is the "duty" of the hospital to seek information available from the data bank in the course of evaluating a physician's application for appointment or reappointment. A hospital will be "presumed" to have the information available from the data bank whether or not it actually requests the information. In an action against a hospital for negligent credentialing, part of the hospital's defense will be to show that it queried the data bank and that no adverse information regarding the physician had been reported or that adverse information had been thoroughly investigated and the appropriate privileges granted.

Because the National Practitioner Data Bank has been in operation only a short time, it is too early to determine whether it will accomplish the purpose Congress articulated. However, physicians are aware of the various reporting obligations and are more reluctant than before to accept adverse actions at the hands of hospital credentialing committees and governing boards, knowing that the information will be reported to the data bank.

Who Must Be Credentialed

In order to fulfill its responsibility for patient safety, the hospital must have a mechanism in place for investigating the education, training, and patterns of practice of each person who participates in the care or treatment of one of the hospital's patients. The mechanism for the hospital's nurses, social workers, therapists, and technicians is the employment process. The hiring department, with the assistance of the human resources function, gathers and verifies the information supplied by applicants for employment, and the managers and supervisors of the department monitor the care provided by employees. Supervisors generally conduct an annual performance evaluation to document an employee's ability to continue to meet the standard of care provided by the hospital. In addition, all the hospital's employees who are licensed must keep their licenses up-to-date.

However, hospitals do not employ many of the people who participate in the care of patients. There must be some mechanism that applies to independent caregivers that serves the same function as the employment process that applies to hospital employees. In addition to physicians who are credentialed through the medical staff process, there are other independent practitioners who treat, diagnose, attend, or otherwise participate in the care of patients. Most commonly, these include dentists, psychologists, podiatrists, nurse midwives, certified and registered nurse anesthetists, chiropractors, and other allied health practitioners. Deciding which of these practitioners are part of the organized medical staff and whether each category of affiliation enjoys the full benefits of membership is the responsibility of the institution's governing board.

In addition to the other information it needs, the governing board must be informed about what the laws of the particular state say about who may be, or who must be, admitted to membership. The professional organizations of some health practitioners have pressured state legislatures to enact statutes prohibiting hospitals from discriminating against them in determining the rights and privileges of medical staff membership. The institution's board may not have the option of rejecting the applications of certain practitioners, regardless of whether the organized medical staff wishes to admit these practitioners to membership, if state law requires that they be granted membership status.

Practitioners who are not employed by the hospital and who are not members of the medical staff but who participate in the care of patients also must be credentialed. For example, if a physician on the staff wants to bring a nurse, social worker, physician assistant, or surgical assistant into the hospital to participate in the care of patients, that person should first present credentials, references, malpractice history, and the other information the hospital has determined it wants to see, to the credentials committee. The practitioner's credentials will be considered, and the hospital will follow its credentialing process for these allied health practitioners before the individual may participate in a patient's care or document care in a patient's chart.

Conflicting Interests in Credentialing

Practitioners seek privileges at hospitals in order to have access to the resources the hospitals provide. For their part, hospitals want enough medical staff members to bring in patients to fill beds and utilize hospital services and equipment. However, to avoid legal liability and to gain accreditation, hospitals must enforce vigorous credentialing procedures for all practitioners who seek privileges before allowing them to take care of patients in their facilities. As they carry out this function, hospitals must be aware of the legal limits that protect applicants for membership and credentials. This section examines some of those legal limits that threaten effective credentialing.

Antitrust Suits

The biggest threat to effective credentialing has been the hospital's and medical staff's fear that a practitioner against whom an adverse credentialing action is contemplated will bring an action under state and federal statutes that prohibit combinations and conspiracies in restraint of trade. Antitrust suits typically name the hospital and the individuals, including the physicians, who participate in the credentialing process. Courts allow these actions to proceed because of the inherent conflict of interest of physicians involved in the credentialing process. The conflict arises because the physicians who examine the qualifications of practitioners applying for privileges are in the same specialty, serve the same community, and would be competing with the applicants for patients. Thus, a physician who files an antitrust suit in a privileges case may claim that the decision to restrict privileges was based on a desire to prevent competition rather than on legitimate concerns about quality of care.

The Health Care Quality Improvement Act (HCQIA) was enacted partly to protect hospitals and physicians against this threat. The HCQIA provides immunity for state and federal antitrust claims for those hospitals following its requirements for providing due process to those physicians against whom an adverse action is recommended.

Rights under the Fourteenth Amendment

A physician who is adversely affected by the hospital's credentialing process may add other causes of action to the antitrust claim. A frequent claim in litigation over privilege denials is that the hospital violated the physician's rights under the Fourteenth Amendment. The Fourteenth Amendment provides that a state may not deprive a person of life, liberty, or property without due process of law, nor deny equal protection under the law. The physician claims that the right to practice in the hospital is a property right. Then the physician must show that the hospital is so closely tied to government that the actions of the hospital are the actions of the state. Many jurisdictions have found that the hospital's receipt of federal funds, primarily through the Medicare and Medicaid programs, is the link that imposes on the hospital a duty to provide due process under the Fourteenth Amendment. If the hospital's medical staff bylaws include the due process provisions specified in HCQIA and the due process provisions were followed in denying privileges, the hospital will defend itself by showing that the physician was granted due process as required by the Constitution.

Allegations of Discrimination

Another cause of action a physician may bring against the hospital and the individuals who participate in the credentialing decision is an allegation of discrimination based on a suspect classification such as race, sex, age, or national origin. The HCQIA specifically excludes protection of hospitals and physicians in discrimination actions. To avoid liability for discrimination, hospital governing boards must be vigilant when they reduce, deny, terminate, or suspend privileges to ensure that the quality of care issues that led to the action are well documented.

Tortious Interference and Defamation

Also included in the litany of actions brought by physicians unhappy with the outcome of a credentialing action are tortious interference with contract and defamation. To prove tortious interference with contract, the physician must show that the hospital's denial of privileges unlawfully interfered with a contractual relationship between the physician and the patient, under which the physician provided medical care. In a defamation action, the physician claims that those involved in reviewing the quality of care provided to the physician's patents made untruthful statements that harmed the physician's reputation. Since the credentialing process requires that physicians on review committees make judgements on other physicians' methods of practicing medicine, reviewer physicians must be careful in wording such statements so that they are not defamatory.

Competition for Privileges

Medicine has become increasingly more specialized, and treatments have become more reliant on innovative, high-technology procedures. As a consequence, competition among medical specialists to be credentialed to perform these procedures has become more intense. For example, several different specialist and subspecialist groups assert that their practitioners are qualified to perform certain cardiac procedures. The most difficult decisions that credentials committees face are deciding what standards of education, training, and experience they should require of an applicant to do procedures that cross medical specialties. A hospital that, at the urging of its cardiology department, limits all procedures involving the heart to physicians who have advanced training in cardiology will likely face an antitrust suit because there may be other training courses that noncardiologists can take to be qualified. The counterbalancing concern for the hospital is to ensure that the standards for angiography, for example, are stringent enough that only those who are competent to perform the procedures, regardless of specialty, will perform them in the facility.

Other Organizations That Credential Physicians

Managed care organizations that limit their physician panels, whether organized by health care providers or insurance companies, also may credential physicians to decide who gets to be on their panels. Generally, their credentialing efforts are less intense than the efforts hospitals make. Many managed care organizations rely on the hospitals they contract with for hospital services to provide them with information for their credentialing decisions. Because most states have laws protecting this information from discovery, hospitals must be very cautious when signing provider contracts with insurance companies, health maintenance organizations (HMOs), and preferred provider organizations (PPOs) if the contracts have clauses requiring them to share physician data. If the hospital does not treat its peer review information as confidential, it may not be able to argue its confidentiality in a malpractice action.

Additionally, managed care organizations are more likely than hospitals to exclude a physician on the basis of the physician's utilization of resources—the practice that physicians call "economic credentialing." Once again, hospitals must be cautious about providing their utilization review data too liberally to outside organizations, because utilization data also may be protected under state statute. In addition, because physician-specific utilization data are extremely sensitive, their release without the physician's consent will cause political problems for the hospital's administration.

Conclusion

As the resources allocated to health care become more scarce, hospitals will continue to be squeezed (1) by physicians, who will continue to push for access to hospital resources and who will wage their battle in court if denied those resources; (2) by patients, who will continue to demand that hospitals monitor physician practice; and (3) by regulators, who will pay less for services while demanding more intensive scrutiny of patient care. The most recent suggestion for health care reform is to place liability for physician malpractice on the organizations that physicians are a part of rather than on individual physicians. If this "enterprise liability" theory is enacted into law, the credentialing function will become far more intensive than it is currently. One key to the fiscal health of the enterprise, whether it be a hospital, an HMO, or an insurance company, will be to credential only those physicians the enterprise is sure will not commit malpractice. Another solution under this scenario is to pass the liability on to outside organizations that the hospital would engage to perform the credentialing function.

Another fact of life for hospitals is that those physicians who provide high-quality care using the fewest or least expensive resources will be the most valuable staff physicians. Hospitals and other health care organizations will use increasingly sophisticated methods of data collection for outcomes research and physician profiling as a means of providing the most effective care for the least amount of money. They will increase the use of this information as an educational tool, and many hospitals also will use it more frequently in credentialing decisions. Hospitals have no choice but to use the tools at their disposal to become much more selective about who is on their medical staff, regardless of whether they decide to hire physicians, to contract exclusively with physician groups, to focus their services by eliminating unprofitable ones, or to allocate the number of physicians in each of the medical services the hospital offers, or a combination of all these techniques. However hospitals choose to handle the credentialing process, their credentials committees will have to become much more aware of the legal and regulatory constraints that protect the physician's right to practice at the same time that hospitals follow their obligation to protect the patient's right to high-quality health care. It is a delicate balance that must be maintained.

References

1. Darling v. Charleston Community Memorial Hospital, 33 Ill. 2d 326, 211 N.E2d 253 (1965), *cert. denied* 383 U.S. 946 (1966).

2. Ibid., at 260.

3. Ibid., at 257.

4. Ibid.

5. Johnson v. Misericordia Community Hospital, 301 N.W.2d 156 (Wis. 1981).

6. Ibid., at 172.

7. Ibid., at 169–170.

8. 132 Cal. App. 3d 183 Cal. Rptr. 156.

9. Ibid., at 345.

10. Ohio Revised Code 3727.02.

11. O.R.C. 3727.03.

12. O.R.C. 3701.351.

13. Bouquett v. St. Elizabeth Corporation, 538 NE.2d 113 (1989).

14. Albain v. Flower Hospital, 553 NE.2d 1038 (1990).

15. 42 U.S.C. Section 11101 et.seq., as amended.

2 Legal Issues

Introduction

A rich body of case law has developed over the past six decades involving the legal requirements for medical staff credentialing. In the landmark case *Hayman v. Galveston*,[1] the United States Supreme Court ruled that physicians do not have a "right" to become a member of the medical staff. However, the Supreme Court did not say that physicians were without any rights in the decision making that leads to a determination about medical staff privileges.

This chapter discusses the legal issues of due process and equal protection and the concept of fairness in according procedural due process for the medical staff, including the adoption of the fair hearing plan. It also outlines the steps involved in taking adverse actions against physicians and describes the appeal process.

Public versus Private Hospital Due Process Requirements

Although over the years the law has recognized that public and government operated hospitals must meet the requirements of due process and equal protection under the Fourteenth Amendment to the Constitution, triggering similar due process and equal protection requirements for private hospitals is not easy. Some courts have indicated that substantial amounts of state and federal funding constitute *state action*, meaning that private hospitals receiving funding must accord physicians due process and equal protection in matters of staff privileges. However, there is a larger body of case law that disagrees. The majority of courts have a much more rigorous test for triggering state action sufficient to require private hospitals to meet due process and equal protection requirements. Typically, this includes a large degree of government involvement in the operation or work of the facility. It also requires a connection between state requirements and the staff privileges action taken against a physician. Further, there must be evidence that demonstrates that the state approves or promotes such requirements.

However, the lines distinguishing public and private hospitals are often blurred by the requirements found in the hospitals' bylaws. Many private hospitals set out in detail due process requirements for credentialing medical staff, processing initial and renewal appointments, and taking corrective action, even if the law does not require them to do so. Thus, their own bylaws become the benchmark or standard against which their actions are judged in handling credentialing and privileging issues.

The distinctions between private and public hospitals may be on the wane in the area of due process considerations. Over the years, federal funding requirements and the regulatory or oversight mechanisms imposed by law have created a more level playing field. Coupled with the actions taken by private hospitals to address the rights of their medical staff "customers," the net effect may well be a private versus public distinction without significant meaning.

Due Process and Equal Protection

As used here, *due process* has two distinct meanings: *Substantive due process* sets out in detail the duties, responsibilities, and rights of the hospital and the physicians whereas *procedural due process* involves the rules of the game or the procedures which the hospital follows to administer the substantive duties and rights of both parties. In addition, hospitals must be cognizant of the equal protection requirements under the law. Unlike due process, *equal protection* refers to prohibiting discrimination on the basis of race, creed, sex, or other factors deemed suspect.

There is little doubt that denial of substantive rights will trigger legal action. For example, if state legislation mandates that doctors of podiatric medicine not be subject to blanket discrimination in appointments to the clinical staff, hospitals that contravene such requirements are likely to find themselves the targets of significant litigation. In essence, the legislation creates a substantive right that accords equal protection or opportunity to practitioners of podiatric medicine to apply for staff privileges.

However, the fact that a state has a nondiscrimination clause prohibiting blanket denial of staff privileges to a class of practitioners does not mean that each and every practitioner who applies is entitled to be appointed to the medical staff. Rather, on an individual basis, the practitioner must meet the requirements delineated in staff bylaws to demonstrate the requisite skills, training, and qualifications needed for a favorable recommendation for appointment to the staff.

There are judicial decisions that can serve as legal guideposts to assist hospitals in steering clear of requirements or activities that may be considered discriminatory. The same can be said of rules or practices that are not reasonably or rationally related to the stated interest of the facility. Credentialing practices that are clear, reasonable, and well articulated are likely to go unchallenged. However, credentialing requirements that are ill defined and that are not subject to objective application are likely to be tested in the courts.

The best approach is to delineate well-accepted professional qualifications for purposes of credentialing and to avoid those topics that are likely to lead to challenges. Credentialing requirements should be linked to the stated mission, goals, and objectives of the hospital. Tied to the hospital's stated objectives should be quality of care and objective professional standards—the hallmarks of "safe" credentialing criteria. Procedures that address the clinician's ability to perform within accepted performance standards are reasonable and therefore not subject to successful challenges based on denial of substantive due process or equal protection.

The Concept of Fairness

To a large extent, the case law that has developed on credentialing and staff privileges has involved denial of procedural due process. Thus, in some states, legislation and regulations have set out detailed requirements for hospitals to follow in according procedural due process to the medical staff.

Hospital bylaws have been influenced by the developments in both case law and legislation. Detailed provisions in the bylaws map out the rights, duties, and obligations of the hospital in handling cases involving denial of an initial appointment or reappointment to the medical staff. Detailed provisions also are found in the bylaws for disciplining those appointed to the staff, including the process to be followed for summary suspension, revocation, or curtailment of privileges.

The focal point of the law and bylaws is the concept of *fairness*. The intent of this concept is to create as level a playing field as possible between the hospital and the physician who is challenging the hospital's decision. Although the intent may be to create an atmosphere of fair play, much depends on how the hospital, the physician, and others apply the rules. For example, on the surface, a set of bylaws may appear to be "fair" and correct from a procedural due process perspective, but as *applied*, a far different analysis may emerge. Thus, to escape a successful challenge, the hospital must ensure not only that the rules are procedurally correct, but also that the application of the bylaws is fair in the context of the circumstances of each case.

Fairness encompasses many criteria. In the context of credentialing, the concept includes notice of the requirements to be met when seeking initial or renewal appointments as well as the criteria on which determinations are made about staff privileges. Fairness extends to an objective evaluation of credentials as measured against objective standards such as licensure, board certification, and demonstrated clinical competence.

Fairness emerges as a key issue when a physician's application for privileges is rejected or a physician is informed that delineated privileges will be less than those requested. Fairness considerations also surface when a physician is the subject of disciplinary or corrective action.

In each of these circumstances, fairness includes several considerations. Following are the most common of these:

1. *Notice:* The physician should receive in writing the reasons for the hospital's decision to reject or restrict his or her appointment to the medical staff. In the case of corrective action, this refers to the reasons for determining why such action was taken.
2. *Hearing:* The physician should have the opportunity to request a hearing before an impartial group within a reasonable time period, meaning that members of the hearing panel must conduct themselves in good faith and make a determination based on only the facts revealed.
3. *Time to prepare:* The hearing should take place after a reasonable period of time has been provided the physician to analyze the basis for the hospital's decision and to mount a challenge to it.
4. *Opportunity to review pertinent hospital documentation:* The physician should have the right to examine — especially in corrective action cases — the documentary information that led to the hospital's determination, including utilization management, peer review, pathology and incident reports.
5. *Opportunity to challenge the hospital's evidence:* The physician should be accorded the opportunity to refute the information put forward by the hospital.
6. *Opportunity to present evidence:* The physician should be given the chance to produce witnesses and documentary information that challenges the decision taken against him or her.
7. *Determination by the hearing panel:* The physician is entitled to a written determination from the hearing panel within a reasonable time after the proceeding is completed. The written determination should be clear and to the point and should be based on the substantial and factual information presented at the hearing.
8. *The right to appeal:* The physician should be afforded the opportunity to appeal the hearing panel's determination within a reasonable period of time.

Two questions that often arise in the context of fairness focus on the physician's right to representation by legal counsel and his or her right to have stenographic recordings made of the proceedings before the hearing panel. Although hospital bylaws frequently recognize the physician's right to representation by legal counsel before the hearing panel, the physician's opportunity to have counsel in the interactions leading to the initial determination is not well addressed.

Those who demand to have the proceedings recorded by a stenographer have in mind the preservation of a good "record" for purposes of an appeal before the court. What must be remembered, however, is that the hearing panel does not operate by the rules of a court. It operates on the basis of fairness without the attention to detail found in the civil rules of procedure or evidence that guide a judicial proceeding. Courts hearing appeals are cognizant of this fact.

Hospitals that demonstrate fairness in the management of credentialing practices and corrective action are likely to be successful. Although their actions may be challenged by physicians, the courts will focus on the hospitals' fairness and attention to due process. Indeed, in most instances, absent a factual indication of denial of due process, the courts are loathe to overturn rulings made by hospitals based on substantive issues. In essence, the courts look to hospitals as the fact finders. As long as the hospitals do their work well, their basic determinations are likely to be left alone by the courts.

The Fair Hearing Plan

To facilitate fairness and to avoid legal challenges based on lack of due process, most hospitals today have embraced the concept of a *fair hearing plan*. A fair hearing plan details both rights and obligations when hospitals decide to deny or restrict a physician's appointment. The plan also describes the procedure the institution is to follow in taking action against a staff physician who lacks the skill or judgment to perform the procedures that have been granted under the credentialing process. Additionally, it maps out the rules to be followed for corrective action.

The medical staff bylaws must make clear that any disciplinary action taken against a physician is done by "a professional review body" or a "peer review committee," that the individuals involved are acting at the direction of this committee and on behalf of the institution, and that only the governing body takes final action. Further, the governing body of the institution is required by law to monitor the quality of medical care provided by physicians who have privileges to practice at the institution. The medical staff standards of the Joint Commission on Accreditation of Healthcare Organizations (JCAHO) require that the medical staff perform this function for the hospital. Standard 1.1 of the section on medical staff says that the medical staff has "overall responsibility for the quality of the professional services provided by individuals with clinical privileges, as well as the responsibility of accounting therefor to the governing body."[2]

As a practical matter, the hospital may find it advantageous to separate the fair hearing plan from the medical staff bylaws. The bylaws provide an organizational structure for the medical staff. In addition, the bylaws outline the qualifications and responsibilities of medical staff membership, the department structure (if there is to be one), the committee structure, and the leadership structure—all characteristics of how the medical staff organizes itself. Any bylaw changes must go first through the medical staff process and then to the hospital's board of trustees for approval. Changes are difficult and require a significant length of time to implement.

The fair hearing plan is not part of the organizational structure of the medical staff but, rather, an internal procedure the purpose of which is to substitute for a legal process in a court of law. The process must be able to be changed quickly to conform to the holdings of the courts as they are published. Thus, separating the fair hearing plan from the bylaws allows the hospital to implement a quicker process for change than the bylaws usually require.

Under the Health Care Quality Improvement Act (HCQIA), the professional review body and the individuals involved in taking action against a member of the medical staff or a physician seeking to join the medical staff must be acting on behalf of the governing body of the institution. It is in the hospital's best interest to view the medical staff as a partner with hospital administration acting on behalf of the hospital's governing body rather than treating the medical staff as a separate entity. However, regardless of the relationship, for the committees and individuals taking peer review action to enjoy immunity under HCQIA, the fair hearing plan must be written so that it complies with the HCQIA stipulation that the medical staff makes recommendations to the governing body and only the governing body takes final action.

Actions by all committees and individuals other than members of the governing body should be termed *findings* or *recommendations* or some other term indicating that the report is not final. Committees should be defined in the fair hearing plan as either professional review bodies or peer review committees, and individuals who serve—whether they are officers, directors, hospital staff, or outside reviewers—should clearly be serving at the committee's direction in order to be protected under the act.

Limits Imposed by the HCQIA

The hospital should limit the due process afforded to the physicians on its medical staff to those outlined in the HCQIA. The fair hearing process should be as simple as possible and yet allow complainants adequate due process. To minimize the drain on time and resources that due process hearings require, hospitals should require that the medical staff due process procedures afford physicians only basic procedural rights. At the first hint of an investigation under the fair hearing plan, the physician being investigated generally will contact a lawyer. Unless the rights of the physician are clearly spelled out and limited to the minimum required to provide due process, medical staff officers and hospital administration may find themselves using all their available time and energy to meet the demands of the physician's attorney. Although the procedure must be fair, it also should conserve, to the extent possible, the hospital resources devoted to the investigation and hearing.

In the context of the medical staff fair hearing process, the HCQIA attempts to provide an outline for courts of what "minimum due process" is, at least for the purpose of protecting the hospital and the participants from liability for antitrust actions. Until there have been more cases decided interpreting the HCQIA, no one knows for certain what the are "minimum" requirements. They may or may not replace the minimum standards required by case law in some jurisdictions, or by legislative enactments for state antitrust actions. The hospital's attorney should be called on to review the fair hearing plan to ensure that it complies with local law. The HCQIA states that minimum due process is at least what is set out in the act. Thus, unless the hospital's attorney advises otherwise, there is no legal requirement to provide more due process than is specified in the HCQIA.

Standards Set by the HCQIA

The HCQIA sets four standards to be met by individuals seeking immunity for peer review actions. An action adverse to the physician must be taken only (1) in the reasonable belief that the action is in the furtherance of high-quality health care, (2) after a reasonable effort has been made to obtain the facts of the matter, (3) after adequate notice and hearing procedures, and (4) in the reasonable belief that the action was warranted by the facts known after a reasonable effort has been made to obtain the facts.

The beginning section of the fair hearing plan of the medical staff bylaws should recite these standards, and in the same section, "the furtherance of high-quality health care" should be defined broadly to include actions against physicians whose actions "have been detrimental to patient care, detrimental to the best interests of the hospital, in violation of the hospital's policies, rules, and regulations, the medical staff's bylaws or rules, or contrary to the standards of practice of the profession."[3]

A recent Ninth Circuit Court decision found that if these standards are met, staff physicians engaged in a professional review action that adversely affects a physician's privileges have immunity for antitrust actions. This is true even when physician peer reviewers act in bad faith.[4]

The Steps Involved in Taking Adverse Actions

A number of steps are involved in the process of recommending that an adverse action be taken against a physician. The following subsections describe these steps beginning with determining whether an investigation is warranted and ending with making final recommendations to the board.

Step 1: Determine Whether an Investigation Is Needed

Before a recommendation adverse to a physician can be taken to the board of trustees, an investigation must be conducted to determine whether there is sufficient evidence on which to base an action. Accusations against physicians are common. They may be brought by jealous competitors, perhaps by a nurse with a personal grudge against a physician unrelated to the quality of the physician's care, or by colleagues whose practice is more conservative or traditional than the questioned physician's. Occasionally, accusations are brought by someone genuinely concerned about the physician's judgment or skill.

Accusers frequently refuse to put their accusations in writing and, in many cases, may decide to remain anonymous. Depending on the seriousness of the accusation, the persons responsible for the safe operation of the institution are the ones who must decide whether to investigate the various rumors and innuendos they hear about a physician's practices. The risk of ignoring an allegation that a patient may ultimately be harmed by a physician who lacks skill or judgment is illustrated by a recent Massachusetts case.[5] In this case, the Massachusetts Supreme Court found that the hospital was not entitled to summary judgment on a negligent credentialing allegation, even though a physician who had been granted privileges by the hospital raped a woman who was not even the hospital's patient. The plaintiff, who was an employee of the hospital, was raped in her home during a house call by the physician. He had held privileges at the defendant hospital for 17 years despite the fact that there had been complaints by patients and staff about incidents of sexual misconduct during that time. The plaintiff sued the hospital for the injuries she sustained as a result of being raped by the physician, alleging that she had relied on the fact that the physician had continued to be granted privileges at the hospital when she established a physician–patient relationship. Because she was employed by the hospital, she was in a position to know whether the hospital had refused or revoked the physician's privileges and would not have sought care from him if the hospital had taken adverse action with respect to the physician's privileges.

The court found that the plaintiff raised a sufficient question of material fact to allow her case to go forward. The court's holding in this case, although limited to the particular facts, nevertheless illustrates the risk of not fully considering allegations of patient or staff abuse in the credentialing process.

On the other hand, the risk of investigating every accusation no matter how farfetched, is that an unnecessary amount of energy will be spent investigating unfounded accusations and perhaps encouraging people to use the process for harassment or revenge. Additionally, such investigations will anger the physicians on the medical staff and will quickly alienate them from hospital administration and the medical staff committee members. Thus, if physicians are constantly the target of investigations, hospital administrators and medical staff leaders will lose the trust of their medical staff members.

The hospital does not commit negligent credentialing if it follows acceptable procedures in granting the physician the appropriate privileges, even if the physician negligently injures a patient. However, if the hospital knows, or should have known, that the physician does not meet the appropriate standard, the hospital may be liable if a patient is harmed because of the physician's negligence. The patient's attorney, by showing that an accusation related to the negligence in question was not investigated, may be able to demonstrate that the hospital was put on notice of the physician's incompetence and did nothing about it.

Step 2: Appoint an Investigating Committee

Once the responsible official, usually the hospital administrator or the chief of the medical staff, or both, has decided that an accusation is substantive enough to be formally investigated, he or she looks to the fair hearing plan to begin the process. The plan should describe a method for appointing a committee to begin a formal investigation into the truth of the allegations. Typically, either the medical executive committee or the credentials committee investigates or has authority to appoint a small ad hoc committee to investigate. Because the accusation may be groundless, the investigation should be done quietly and involve only a few people in order to minimize damage to both the physician's reputation and the hospital administration's credibility with physicians. Thus, the persons appointed to the committee must be able to be trusted to maintain strict confidentiality.

It is equally important that the investigating committee move with all due speed. The fair hearing plan should specify that the committee present its recommendation within 60 days. Unless summarily suspended, the physician should be allowed to continue to practice to the full extent of privileges during the investigation.

While the investigation is being conducted, the physician's attorney should not be allowed to interfere. At this early stage, no adverse action has been recommended or taken and, if the accusation is found to be groundless, no adverse action will be taken. If the physician's attorney tries to become involved during the investigation, the person whose function it is to oversee the fair hearing procedure should inform the attorney of the expected order of events and promise to notify both the physician and his or her attorney if and when there is an adverse recommendation.

The investigators may choose not to inform the physician that the investigation is being conducted. However, if the committee finds that there may be some basis to the charges it is investigating, it probably should choose to ask for the physician's version of events, although it is not required to so.

Including the Risk Manager

The risk manager may be called on to advise those who are involved in the investigation. The moment an issue arises that requires an investigation and that could lead to an action against the physician, the risk manager's role is to ensure that the involved physician gets the full benefit of the due process procedures in the bylaws, that the confidentiality of the proceeding is maintained, that the hospital's insurance carriers are put on notice at the proper time, and that the hospital's attorney is consulted before any official notice is given to the physician. In some instances, the bylaws may not be specific enough to explain what the procedure should be under the particular set of facts. For example, the bylaws may not explain how to proceed if the chief executive officer (CEO) receives an anonymous note that the physician is an alcoholic. The risk manager, in consultation with the hospital's attorney, must advise the leadership on how to proceed under the institution's documents and federal and state law. Proper documentation that all the steps were followed is essential, because an action against a physician leads almost inevitably to a lawsuit. The risk manager must make sure that everything that is put in writing will, to the extent possible, further the hospital's defense.

The risk manager also should resist any attempt by the physician to solicit the risk manager's counsel. The risk manager works for the institution, and if the institution is investigating evidence of the physician's failure to meet the hospital's standards, the physician and the hospital become adversaries. Risk managers who have developed a good rapport with physicians may find that physicians want to enlist them in the fight against the hospital. After ensuring that the physician has a copy of the procedure, the risk manager's role is to advise only the hospital and medical staff personnel who are taking action against the physician. This process follows from the risk manager's duty to the hospital and the ethical principles set forth by the American Society for Healthcare Risk Management.

Using Peer Review Information in the Investigation

Under the laws of most states, information developed through the quality assurance/peer review process is protected from discovery. However, in order to invoke this protection, hospitals must treat the information as protected, according to the dictates of their state's statute. Peer review information may be useful in investigating allegations against physicians, but hospital attorneys and risk managers must be consulted during any investigation to determine whether the use of this information will jeopardize the confidentiality of the hospital's peer review process.

The physician being investigated may wish to use favorable peer review information as a defense. However, because such use may violate the confidentiality of the peer review process and because the information belongs to the hospital and not to the physicians or a particular physician, it is up to the hospital to decide how or whether to make the information available for the physician's use. If the hospital chooses to use peer review information to support a decision to take an adverse action against the physician, the hospital will be required to allow the physician to use additional peer review data to defend against the allegations. It would violate fundamental fairness to refuse the physician access to all the data under these circumstances.

An alternative method is to have a review of the physician's medical charts done by physicians not associated with the hospital. Because it is difficult to enlist physician reviewers who work in the same community with the physician under investigation, one approach may be to have the charts reviewed by physicians in other communities in the state or in other states. Thus, the hospital will have the advantage of having the review done by physicians in the same specialty as the physician under investigation but who cannot be accused of being in competition with that physician.

The disadvantage is that such reviews are expensive. The reviewer probably will not be someone the risk manager or medical staff leadership has worked with in the past, and thus the hospital cannot know in advance whether it is getting what it expected from the external source. For example, the physician may not be familiar with local methods of practice or with the kinds of equipment used by local physicians. Physicians from large medical centers have the appropriate credentials to impress a judge and jury, but may have no idea what physicians who practice in rural areas or small community hospitals face from day to day in their practices. Consequently, in some cases, applying the standards of an out-of-town physician to the practice of a local physician may be misleading to the hospital and unfair to the physician.

Step 3: Request Action against the Physician

If the investigating committee finds sufficient grounds upon which to bring an action against a physician, it should present its findings in writing to the committee responsible for recommendations regarding physician privileges, normally the executive committee of the medical staff or the credentials committee. The findings should include the issues, the facts surrounding the issues, committee recommendations, and the rationale for the recommendations. The recommendations will be either that:

- There is no credible evidence on which to base an action.
- The physician should be warned or reprimanded.
- The physician should be placed on probation or the physician's privileges should be limited in some specified way.
- The physician's privileges should be reduced, modified, or suspended in some specified way.
- The physician should be monitored in some specified way during the delivery of patient care at the hospital.
- The physician's membership on the medical staff should be suspended or revoked or the physician should be put on probation.
- Some other specified action should be taken against the physician.

If the findings come from an ad hoc committee appointed by the executive committee, the executive committee sends a recommendation to the CEO who then transmits it to the institution's board of trustees for action.

Step 4: Send the Required Notice

The medical staff bylaws should spell out any adverse action that does not entitle the physician to a hearing. Some actions taken by the medical staff do not require that the physician who is the subject of the action be given a hearing. For example, the bylaws should state that if the physician relinquishes or loses the license to practice, privileges on the medical staff are automatically terminated. In this instance, the only issue is whether the physician actually has lost the license to practice. Examples of automatic relinquishment of privileges may include failure to complete records in a timely fashion or failure to carry the minimum required malpractice insurance. Many hospital-based physicians, such as anesthesiologists, radiologists, and pathologists, have agreed to a provision in their contract with the hospital that their membership on the medical staff and privileges to practice at the hospital will be automatically terminated if the contract expires or is otherwise terminated. Loss of membership and privileges under these circumstances does not trigger a hearing. Additionally, if an investigating committee's recommendation falls short of some adverse effect on membership or privileges, such as a recommendation that a physician take continuing education courses in a specific area or that the physician's procedures be monitored by another physician for a period of time, the physician is not necessarily entitled to a hearing.

Usually, however, the committee's recommendation does adversely affect the physician's privileges. A recommendation to reduce, suspend, restrict, deny, or terminate a physician's membership or clinical privileges may be made, or the physician may be required to have a coadmitter or take certain continuing education courses before being allowed to perform certain procedures. In these instances, the physician has a right to a hearing, and at this stage, must receive notice under the HCQIA that an adverse action has been proposed. The notice must state that a professional review action has been proposed and give the reasons for it, must indicate that the physician has the right to a hearing and set the time limit (30 days or more) within which to request such a hearing, and must include a summary of the physician's due process rights afforded if a hearing is requested.

The due process rights to be included in the notice should be spelled out in the fair hearing plan. They are defined in the HCQIA and include at least the following:

A. The hearing shall be held before an arbitrator mutually acceptable to the physician and the health care entity, or before a hearing officer appointed by the hospital and not in direct competition with the physician, or before a panel of individuals appointed by the hospital who are not in direct competition with the physician

B. That the right to a hearing is forfeited if the physician fails, without good cause, to appear

C. That the physician has a right to be represented by an attorney or other person of the physician's choosing

D. That a record shall be made of the proceeding which the physician may request a copy of if the physician pays the reasonable costs

E. That the physician may call, examine, and cross-examine witnesses

F. That the physician may present evidence that is relevant

G. That the physician may submit a written statement at the close of the hearing

H. That the physician shall receive a copy of the hearing panel, hearing officer's or arbitrator's recommendation

I. That the physician shall receive a written decision of the health care entity, including the basis for the decision.[6]

If the CEO does not receive a request for a hearing within the specified time, the physician's right to a hearing is waived. If the request for a hearing is received, the HCQIA requires that a second written notice be given to the physician. Additionally, certain items of information must be included in this second notice, including the date and time of the hearing (which must be held at least 30 days or more after the date of the notice) and a list of the witnesses who will be called on behalf of the hospital to present evidence.

In addition to stating the due process rights of the physician, the fair hearing plan also should state what rights are not included at this stage. If the physician's attorney is a litigator, he or she may demand the same kind of pretrial discovery allowed under the civil rules of court. Completing interrogatories and taking depositions of witnesses are not appropriate for the procedure contemplated under the fair hearing plan. Not only should the plan state specifically that the physician does not have the right to pretrial discovery, but it also should limit the physician's right to contact witnesses in advance, unless so allowed by the hearing officer. In addition, depending on the laws of the state, the physician probably will not have access to reports and records of the quality assurance and utilization review committee. However, the physician may assert the right to review patient records in the original and these may be the records used by the quality assurance committee.

Step 5: Appoint the Hearing Panel

The hospital should appoint a hearing panel consisting of physicians, none of whom is in direct competition with the physician under investigation, and a hearing officer, who is usually an independent local attorney who will advise the hearing committee but have no vote on the outcome. The individual responsible for appointing the hearing panel is the hospital's CEO, with advice from the chief of the medical staff.

Having an independent hearing officer appointed to determine procedural rules relieves the members of the panel from having to determine both procedure and outcome. Although, the hearing officer usually is a local attorney, having an attorney serve in this role is not required. The hearing officer will rule on such issues as the evidence that may be admitted, the order of the procedure, and the challenges and objections to the rules. It may be helpful to have a "prehearing" conference with the legal representatives of both sides to determine procedural issues that may be in dispute.

If an attorney serves as the hearing officer, he or she may not be someone who has been the hospital's advisor on medical staff issues. The panel recommending the action on behalf of the hospital probably will have an attorney advising it or presenting evidence at the hearing. This person may be an attorney who provides counsel to the hospital.

Step 6: Record the Hearing

The HCQIA says that the physician is entitled to have a recording made of the hearing and to have a copy, but must pay the reasonable costs. The hospital may believe that a tape recording will serve the purpose. However, tape recordings may not be dependable enough. Sometimes tapes are accidentally erased or lost, or the tape recorder stops functioning during the hearing without participants being aware of it. Court reporters, as long as they actually show up as scheduled, are more dependable.

The reporter will record the hearing but will not transcribe the recording unless one of the parties orders a transcription, which is an added expense. Neither party should order the hearing to be transcribed unless it becomes necessary for one party or the other to have a written transcript in order to pursue an appeal. Although the statute does not say who will bear the cost of the transcription, it would seem logical to require the party who wants the transcription to pay the costs. If the hearing panel's verdict is appealed on the grounds that the hearing did not provide due process, it is in the interests of both parties to share the expense of transcription. As a rule, the hospital should hire a court reporter to record the hearing, but should not order a transcription unless one is requested by the physician, who must then bear all or part of the costs.

Step 7: Make a Recommendation to the Board

The hearing panel makes its recommendation to the hospital CEO who then forwards it to the board of trustees for final action. In some hospitals, the medical executive committee appoints the hearing committee, receives the recommendation, evaluates the findings or recommendation, and transmits its own recommendation to the CEO, who then transmits it to the board for final action. The bylaws should state a time limit, normally 10 days, within which the hearing panel's written report and recommendation are to be forwarded. Under the HCQIA, the physician is given the right to receive the written recommendation of the arbitrator, hearing officer, or hearing panel, including a statement of the basis for the recommendation.

The Appeal Process

The grounds for an appeal should be limited to an assertion that the fair hearing procedures were not followed or that the record of the hearing demonstrates on its face that the decision was not supported by substantial evidence. Although the HCQIA does not require that the physician be allowed to appeal the decision of the hearing panel, arbitrator, or hearing officer, the institution is well advised to devise a simple appeal procedure to prevent injustice and protect itself from claims of lack of due process. However, the appeal process of the bylaws must be carefully written and the institution must strictly interpret and follow the bylaws to prevent the appeal process from becoming unwieldy. The tendency of those who want to ensure that physicians have the maximum protection tend to layer appeal upon appeal, or they draft the appeal process to allow it to repeat all the steps of the initial hearing. The purpose of an appeal is only to review the process that was followed at the hearing to ensure that the physician's rights were not violated or, if additional protection is desirable, to ensure that the decision reflects the substantial weight of the evidence, as demonstrated by the hearing record. The appeal procedures should never allow either the hospital or the physician to repeat the evidentiary hearing.

A well-written, simple procedure states the time limit within which the appeal must be requested or the appeal is waived. Either the physician or the institution should have the right to appeal the recommendation to the board. The request for appeal should be made to the CEO, who shall transmit it to the board. The board may either consider the appeal or appoint an ad hoc committee to consider it. As mentioned previously, the members of the committee considering the appeal should not be in direct economic competition with the physician or have any other conflict of interest, such as a well-known personal grudge of long standing. If the basis of the appeal is that the fair hearing process was not followed, no reason exists to require that the ad hoc committee be composed of physicians.

The bylaws should require that the request for appeal state the basis for it. The appeal is most expeditiously handled when the parties are required to pursue it by written statements rather than by oral argument. Within a reasonable period of the request for the appeal (such as 10 days), the physician who has requested the appeal should submit a written statement detailing those facts and procedures he or she believes have prevented a fair hearing. The executive committee or the CEO who is opposing the physician also may submit a written statement, which should be received by the board or the ad hoc committee within a stated number of days before the appellate review. The bylaws should state appropriate time limits within which the appellate review should occur.

The appellate review will consist of the ad hoc committee or the board considering the written statements of the parties. Due process does not require that the parties be present or have a right to make oral arguments. If the bylaws so state, or if the board or the ad hoc committee wishes, oral arguments may be heard. However, the arguments should be limited to no more than 15 minutes or, at a maximum, 30 minutes for each side. The review body also may be given the discretion to ask questions of the parties

Final Action by the Board

Within a time limit stated in the bylaws, usually 30 to 60 days after the appellate review or after the time has expired to request such review, the institution's board will make its decision. This action will complete the procedure provided by the fair hearing plan, and the board's decision is final. If the board's action is adverse to the physician, the decision will immediately affect the physician's privileges. It is this action that is reportable to the state medical board and the National Practitioner Data Bank. Under the HCQIA, the physician is also entitled to receive a copy of the written decision of the board, including a statement of the basis for the decision reached by the board.

Because the board has final authority with regard to all actions approving, suspending, reducing, or revoking medical staff privileges, it also may take any of these actions on its own without any action on the part of hospital administration or the medical staff, and the medical staff bylaws should provide for action by the board independent of the medical executive committee. However, only in extraordinary situations when the board believes such action is justified and the administration or medical staff is either unable or unwilling to act should the board short-circuit the ordinary process. When the board does take unilateral action, it also must provide the due process protections to the affected physician that the bylaws specify.

Summary Suspension

The hospital may summarily suspend a physician's privileges, but it should do so only in those instances when failure to take the action may result in an imminent danger to the health or welfare of a patient. Unlike the usual course of a hearing and appeal during which a physician may continue to exercise privileges until a final board action, the summarily suspended physician may not admit or treat patients until and unless privileges are reinstated. Because the privileges granted to physicians may be considered by courts to be property rights that should not be terminated without due process, a hospital that summarily suspends a physician's privileges must be prepared to provide evidence that the summary suspension was justified on the basis of safe patient care.

Some hospitals are too hasty in using summary suspensions, fearing that they will be sued for negligent credentialing if they do not suspend a physician's privileges when allegations of substandard care are raised. Although there may be some risk in allowing the physician to continue to practice, there is a greater risk of a suit from a physician when the procedures in the bylaws are not closely followed. The danger to the patient should be immediate before a physician's privileges may be summarily suspended. For example, if Dr. Sheila X, an obstetrician, is being investigated for performing more caesarean sections than her colleagues, she must be allowed to continue her practice during the course of the investigation and any subsequent proceeding. This allegation in itself does not show that any of Dr. X's patients are placed in immediate jeopardy by her continuing to exercise privileges. If, on the other hand, when Dr. X. appears in surgery to perform a caesarean, she behaves erratically and smells of alcohol, she must be stopped from doing the surgery. Another instance when a physician's privileges may be suspended is if he or she deliberately exceeds the scope of privileges granted, particularly if the physician has done so on more than one occasion and has been reprimanded. To protect the safety of patients, the hospital's only recourse is to suspend privileges until an investigation has been conducted and a hearing been held.

The Mechanics of Summary Suspension

The medical staff bylaws should specify who may summarily suspend all or a portion of a physician's privileges. Usually, the chief medical officer, the CEO, the chair of the credentials committee, or the chief of the physician's department are named.

The bylaws should state that, at a minimum, any *two* of the individuals mentioned are required. The CEO then notifies the physician that privileges have been suspended, that the suspension is effective immediately, and that the suspension will remain in effect until the medical executive committee modifies or revokes it, after either an investigation or the due process hearing. Once the physician has been summarily suspended, the hospital then follows the due process procedure as outlined in the bylaws.

Reporting a Summary Suspension under the HCQIA

The HCQIA requires that, if a physician's privileges are suspended for longer than 30 days, the suspension must be reported to the National Practitioner Data Bank. This requirement poses problems for hospitals that follow the same procedure in summary suspension cases that they do in all other cases of privilege disputes. Investigations cannot be completed, recommendations cannot be made, hearings cannot be held, and boards cannot act in fewer than 30 days. If the bylaws say that a summary suspension may be invoked before an investigation is done but only when the health of a patient may be in danger, it seems clear that it is a precautionary measure meant not to accuse a physician of substandard practice, but only to protect the welfare of patients while an investigation of the event is conducted. The bylaws should state that a summary suspension is not a final action, but is only precautionary. Because a recent supplement to the *National Practitioner Data Bank Guidebook*[7] suggests that what the bylaws say can determine whether summary suspension is reportable, that section of the bylaws should be carefully drafted so that the bylaws clearly state that summary suspensions are used only as precautions until a final determination can be made.

Conclusion

Most of the case law that has evolved on medical staff credentialing has involved denial of procedural due process. Hospitals have responded to legislation and regulations by incorporating due process provisions in their bylaws.

Today, most hospitals have adopted the concept of the fair hearing plan in which the rights and obligations of both the hospital and the medical staff are spelled out, as are the procedures to be followed in the event an action is brought by the hospital against a physician either rejected for appointment or denied reappointment, and the rules to be followed when the hospital takes disciplinary action against a staff physician.

For the protection of both hospital and physician, action is taken only after a recommendation to do so has been made by an investigating committee appointed by the CEO. The physician has a legal right to produce evidence in his or her defense before a hearing panel, which then makes its recommendation through the CEO to the hospital board for final action. If the physician wishes to contest the board's decision, he or she has the right to appeal within a specified period of time.

However, hospitals with credentialing practices that are clear, reasonable, and well defined are unlikely to have their decisions challenged. This will be particularly true for those hospitals whose credentialing practices are in line with the institution's mission, goals, and objectives and its determination to provide high-quality care and to maintain objective performance standards.

References

1. Hayman v. Galveston, 273 U.S. 414 (1927).

2. Joint Commission on Accreditation of Healthcare Organizations. *The Accreditation Manual for Hospitals.* Oakbrook Terrace, IL: JCAHO, 1992, p. 55.

3. 42 U.S.C. §1112(a) (1988).

4. Austin v. McNamara, CA 9, No. 90-55333, 11/6/92.

5. Copithorne v. Framingham Union Hospital, 401 Mass. 860, 1986.

6. 42 U.S.C. §1112(b) (1988).

7. United States Department of Health and Human Services. *National Practitioner Data Bank Guidebook.* Supplement: Current References for Data Users. Washington, DC: HSS, 1992.

3 Key Participants and Their Responsibilities

Introduction

The medical staff credentialing process involves the participation of several key players within the hospital organization. These include the institution's governing board, administration, and medical staff serving on the medical executive committee and the credentials committee. In addition, various departments and services may be called on to provide specialty information needed to establish credentialing criteria. All of these participants will be affected in one way or another by the credentialing determinations eventually made by the governing board as it attempts to ensure that the hospital's patients receive high-quality, cost-effective medical care.

This chapter identifies the key participants in the credentialing process and discusses their roles and relationships. Additionally, it discusses the process of evaluating applicants for initial privileges and those seeking reappointment to the medical staff.

The Governing Body

The governing body of the health care institution makes all decisions regarding what medical services will be offered to the institution's patients, when a medical service has a sufficient number of practitioners credentialed, who will be appointed to the institution's medical staff, and what procedures each medical staff member can perform within the institution. Most hospitals are organized as corporations governed by boards of directors when incorporated as for-profit organizations or by boards of trustees when incorporated as not-for-profit organizations. The local board of trustees of hospitals that are part of a health care system may be subordinate to a parent company board, in which case the organizing documents of the institution will specify what authority has been reserved to the parent board or delegated to the local board.

The organizational structure of the hospital corporation, including the institution's relationship to the organized medical staff, is set out in the hospital's articles of incorporation or its bylaws sometimes called its constitution or code of regulations, depending on the state's corporation laws. In exercising governance responsibility, hospital boards must comply with the state's corporation laws and, if accredited by the Joint Commission on Accreditation of Healthcare Organizations (JCAHO), with JCAHO standards set out for the governing bodies of health care organizations. JCAHO standards require that the governing body be responsible for establishing policy, maintaining high-quality patient care, and providing for institutional management and planning.[1]

The boards of most hospitals are made up of citizens from the community served by the hospital. JCAHO standards do not require that a member of the medical staff be a voting member of the governing board, but do require that medical staff members be eligible for membership (GB 1.3) and that the medical staff be represented at meetings (GB 1.4). The standards further state that governing body committees must include medical staff members if the committees deliberate issues affecting the medical staff (G.B. 1.2.4.5). These committees need not include members of the governing board unless their inclusion is required by the hospital's bylaws or the state's corporation laws.

The governing body delegates responsibility for the day-to-day operation of the organization to an individual or individuals, usually the institution's chief executive officer (CEO). This individual may or may not be a member of the board and may or may not have a vote, depending on the organization's bylaws and state law. In most instances, the CEO is not a physician but, rather, an administrator whose education and experience are in managing the policy and financial aspects of health care institutions. Additionally, the CEO acts as liaison between the hospital's senior management, the medical staff, and the board.

The Governing Body's Relationship to the Medical Staff and Administration

JCAHO standards require that the medical staff be organized and responsible to the governing body for the quality of care provided by those who have clinical privileges (MS. 1). The medical staff sets out its organizational structure in the medical staff bylaws, which also describe the requirements to become a member of the medical staff, the rights and responsibilities of membership, the duties of medical staff officers and how they are selected, the duties of medical staff committees and how they are selected, and the mechanism for delineation of clinical privileges. An important function of the medical staff is to ensure that any recommendations made are consistent with its bylaws.

The facility's board appoints both the hospital's chief executive officer (CEO) and the hospital's medical staff. The CEO is authorized by the board to implement the programs and achieve the goals set by the board, including organizing the internal administrative structure, controlling costs, enhancing revenues, and maintaining the physical plant.

One of the great challenges facing any hospital CEO is to balance the demands of the medical staff with the hospital's need to comply with regulatory restraints and to maintain its budget. Physicians on the staff resist any step taken by the hospital that they perceive will interfere with their prerogative to treat their patients according to their best medical judgment. In the performance of their critical functions, the administration and the medical staff frequently clash over who should make decisions about patient care. It is the governing body's responsibility to integrate information provided by the CEO and the medical staff in order to make decisions that will meet the institution's duty to provide high-quality, cost-effective care for the hospital's patients. The board of the institution must understand not only the responsibilities of each, but also communicate those responsibilities clearly to the hospital and its medical staff in order to minimize friction.

The Board's Responsibility for Credentialing

Responsibility for the quality of patients' medical care and for credentialing physicians who practice in the institution rests with the governing body.[2] The Supreme Court of Wisconsin articulated the legal standard when it said that "[t]he hospital's failure to exercise that degree of care, skill and judgment that is exercised by the average hospital in approving an applicant's request for privileges is negligence."[3]

Key Participants and Their Responsibilities

The JCAHO requires that "all individuals who are permitted by law and by the hospital to provide patient care services independently in the hospital have delineated clinical privileges, whether or not they are members of the medical staff" (MS. 4.1). It further requires that "there is a mechanism to assure that all individuals with clinical privileges provide services within the scope for privileges granted" (MS. 4.1.3).

The JCAHO requires that each accredited institution have an executive committee of the medical staff composed mostly of active medical staff members. Among the committee's responsibilities is the requirement that it make recommendations "directly to the governing body for its approval" (GB. 1.11) on two credentialing functions. The first is the mechanism by which membership and privileges are to be decided. The medical staff bylaws will specify this mechanism, which will include such things as the minimum standards required for membership, which committees review and make recommendations on applications, and the board's responsibility to take all final actions on membership and privilege.

The executive committee's second credentialing responsibility is to make recommendations to the governing board regarding which specific individuals will be appointed to the medical staff and what privileges each applicant will be granted (MS. 4.1.2). The standards require the governing body to act on recommendations for appointments, reappointments, terminations of appointments, and the granting of clinical privileges and to resolve any differences in recommendations concerning membership and privileges "within a reasonable period of time" (GB. 1.12 and GB. 1.13). Responsibility for making such recommendations requires an intensive effort not only by members of the medical staff who serve on the committees that make the recommendations, but also by the administrative staff of the hospital, who usually provide support services to the medical executive committee to get the job done.

The Medical Staff Credentials Committee

Because appropriate credentialing is so critical to the quality of care in the facility, the medical staff bylaws in many facilities establish a special standing credentials committee whose members are members of the medical staff and whose sole purpose is to determine first what the standards ought to be for both membership and credentials and then to apply those standards in considering applications for membership and credentials. The credentials committee makes these recommendations to the medical executive committee, which will in turn consider them and submit its own recommendations to the institution's board, which will act on credentialing decisions.

The credentials committee should be an interdisciplinary committee made up of members of the active staff who are willing to devote the time and attention necessary to learn the legal and regulatory requirements of the credentialing function. It is increasingly important that the committee be interdisciplinary because many of the medical procedures that physicians want to do in the institution may be done by physicians in more than one specialty. Thus, an effective committee will have members from many disciplines to set minimum requirements for credentialing physicians across medical specialties.

Establishing Standards for Membership and Credentials

The inherent conflict of interest in the entire credentialing process is evident in the deliberations of the credentials committee. First, it is accepted that only a physician is qualified to evaluate the qualifications of another physician to perform requested procedures. Second, those who are evaluating the physician's qualifications are likely to be his or her competitors because, if they are in the same specialty, they will be providing care to the same patient population. Because physicians in different specialties can perform the same procedures, the conflict cannot be resolved by using physicians in other specialties to evaluate a physician's qualifications. Therefore, the key to successful credentialing is to ensure the objectivity of the credentialing process and the credentials committee's procedures and to enforce this objectivity rigidly.

One key to objectivity is for the board to set minimum standards for membership and credentials in each medical specialty *before* considering applications from physicians. If a physician requests credentials to perform a technologically advanced procedure that has not been done in the institution before, the credentials committee must set aside the application and develop standards by which to evaluate all physicians who may apply to perform that procedure in the future. After the minimum qualifications have been approved by the board, each applicant seeking privileges to perform the new procedure will be considered.

The second key to objectivity is to apply the same standards equally to all applicants although sometimes this can be difficult to do. For example, some institutions have board-approved medical staff development plans that specify how many physicians in each specialty the board believes the facility can provide appropriate resources for. When the institution has granted membership and credentials to the number of physicians in that category on the active staff, no more applications will be accepted for that specialty until either the board decides to increase the number of physicians in that specialty or a vacancy is created when someone currently on staff resigns or is otherwise terminated. Thus, if the cardiology staff is currently closed, the credentials committee will simply not consider applications from cardiologists, but will hold all applications and consider them in the order received when a vacancy occurs. This procedure is used for all cardiologists who apply regardless of how well qualified they may be. This method of considering applications becomes especially difficult if the applicant is a new member of a large group practice, all of whose physicians are currently on the hospital's staff and who admit the largest volume of heart procedures to the facility. However, the objective response is to consider the physician's application only when a vacancy occurs in the cardiology staff and then only after other applications have been processed that were received earlier than the physician's in question.

Exceptions to the established credentialing process should be made rarely, if ever, and then only if safe patient care demands that an exception be made. For example, if the qualifications set by the board for performing obstetrical procedures in the hospital include a requirement that the physician be board certified or board eligible in obstetrics, the credentials committee may not consider the application of an otherwise qualified physician who is not board eligible or board certified in obstetrics. Of course, the board could reconsider the requirement of board certification or eligibility if the requirement is too restrictive, but no applications from physicians requesting obstetrical privileges should be considered until a new standard for considering such applications is determined.

Obtaining Credentialing Information from Departments and Services

Although the credentials committee is responsible for recommending to the executive committee the criteria for evaluating physician applicants for each procedure or level of privileges, it may not always have the information it needs to develop the criteria. Thus, it must rely on each individual department to learn what education, training, and experience physicians should have in order to be granted privileges in that department.

In obstetrics, for example, the credentials committee relies on the OB/GYN service or department to learn the level of training and experience necessary to approve physicians for level I, the most basic procedures; level II, the basic procedures and intermediate procedures; or level III, all the procedures in levels I and II plus the advanced procedures in the field. The credentials committee must assimilate and evaluate the information and formulate its recommendation to the medical executive committee, which will then consider the service's recommendation in formulating its own recommendation to the governing body. Ultimately, the governing body will establish the criteria against which applicants' education, training, and experience will be measured.

When the credentials committee is considering criteria for credentialing physicians to do a procedure that physicians in other departments claim to be theirs exclusively, the committee will evaluate information from all the departments that know the procedure in order to formulate a recommendation. For example, the criteria for performing endoscopies must be based on information from several specialties, including internal medicine, surgery, and family medicine, each of which believes that its physicians are capable of performing endoscopic procedures.

Recently, the American Society for Gastrointestinal Endoscopy and the American College of Gastroenterology published their revised statement on granting hospital privileges to perform gastrointestinal endoscopy. Although they recognize that endoscopy is a multidisciplinary procedure, they nevertheless propose that anyone performing these procedures have formal fellowship or residency training in gastroenterology or surgery, or training and experience commensurate with prerequisites to board eligibility in gastroenterology and gastrointestinal surgery. Although the credentials committee must consider this information when developing criteria for endoscopic privileges, it also should consider information from other services that believe their practitioners are qualified to perform endoscopies. After considering all relevant information, the committee should develop criteria that will allow all qualified practitioners to perform the procedure and that will result in safe, cost-effective patient care.

Evaluating Applicants for Membership and Privileges

After making its recommendations on credentialing criteria to the executive committee, the credentials committee then follows through with its responsibility to evaluate the qualifications of individual applicants against the criteria approved by the board. It evaluates not only first-time applicants, but also applicants for reappointment. In *Johnson v. Misericordia*, the court articulated this role of the credentials committee:

> The credentials committee ... must investigate the qualifications of applicants. ... [A] hospital should, at a minimum, require completion of the application and verify the accuracy of the applicant's statements, especially in regard to his medical education, training and experience. Additionally, it should: (1) solicit information from the applicant's peers, including those not referenced in his application, who are knowledgeable about his education, training, experience, health, competence and ethical character; (2) determine if the applicant is currently licensed to practice in this state and if his licensure or registration has been or is currently being challenged; and (3) inquire whether the applicant has been involved in any adverse malpractice action and whether he has experienced a loss of medical organization membership or medical privileges or membership at any other hospital. The investigating committee must also evaluate the information gained through its inquiries and make a reasonable judgment as to the approval or denial of each application for staff privileges.[4]

The Health Care Quality Improvement Act adds to these steps an inquiry to the National Practitioner Data Bank regarding adverse malpractice judgments or settlements and suspensions, revocations, reductions, or terminations of privileges. The information gathered by the hospital is put into a credentialing file that goes to the credentials committee for evaluation. First, the information comes from the applicant who submits it on the approved application form for membership and privileges or on the approved form for reappointment. Then, if the application is for reappointment, additional information is requested from the applicant's department. If the application is for first-time appointment, information is requested from other institutions where the applicant has practiced; from educational institutions, residency programs, and licensing and regulatory agencies; and from the applicant's peers and supervising physicians.

Administration

The evaluation of applicants involves the gathering of data and the subsequent evaluation of the information. Data gathering is a clerical function and is usually performed by administrative personnel employed by the hospital. The number of employees required depends on the size of the medical staff, but in most hospitals of more than 100 beds, one or more full-time-equivalent employees are devoted exclusively to processing applications for first-time appointments and for reappointments. Either the CEO of the institution or a designated senior administrative representative oversees the credentialing process and attends meetings of the credentials committee to provide guidance and to monitor the committee's objectivity and thoroughness. As the credentialing function becomes more complicated and more critical to the institution's success, the information-gathering function becomes more labor intensive. Some institutions require that at least a part of the expense of gathering information be shared by the medical staff, through either a contribution of a portion of the medical staff dues or a fee to be paid by those applying for appointment or reappointment. However, imposing a fee or other expense sharing can be politically difficult for the CEO or the institution's board.

Another method for reducing the personnel costs of data gathering is to participate in a cooperative venture with other institutions who are evaluating the same physician for privileges. In some areas, hospitals have entered into cooperative ventures with the local medical society or another organization that, for a fee, will perform the clerical functions involved in credentialing. These cooperative ventures have not been widely used by hospitals, because either the service is not cost-effective, the service performed is limited, or the hospital remains legally responsible for data gathering and evaluation regardless of who actually performs the function. Hospitals believe they have better control over their own employees conducting the credentialing process than they have through contracting with some other organization.

Quality Assurance and Utilization Review Committees

Each applicant for reappointment will have a file, usually separate from the credentialing file, that contains information about the physician compiled by the institution's quality assurance and utilization review committees. The purpose of compiling such information is to assist the institution in improving the quality of patient care by keeping the physician and the institution informed about the quality and effectiveness of the physician's practice in the institution. This information must be considered by the credentials committee, the medical executive committee, and the board in evaluating an applicant for reappointment and privileges. If the information is favorable, the applicant will be approved. If the information is adverse or uninformative, committee members and the board must use their judgment in deciding whether the applicant should be approved and what credentials the applicant should be granted. In the case of uninformative data, it may be necessary to gather additional details prior to making a decision on the applicant's request for reappointment to the medical staff. The board may decide to reject the applicant, to condition approval on additional education or training in a particular procedure, to require monitoring during a probationary period, or to impose any other requirement the board believes will protect the institution's patients.

The Evaluation Phase

The evaluation phase of the credentialing process occurs only when the applicant's file is complete; that is, when all information available from the institution has been received, all evaluations have been returned, all queries have been answered, and all licensure and Drug Enforcement Agency information has been verified. The members of the credentials committee must then use their professional judgment to determine whether the applicant is qualified to be a member of the medical staff and what privileges the applicant should be granted.

If the file contains information adverse to the applicant, the committee has a duty to investigate the information until it believes it can make a well-informed determination. For example, if a physician reports a pending lawsuit, the committee may not simply reject the applicant because of the suit, nor may the committee ignore the information. Instead, it must find out what were the circumstances and whether the fact that the suit was brought indicates that the physician's practice in a particular area is substandard. In some institutions, credentials committees require the physician to meet with the committee or a member of the committee as part of the application process. However, in larger institutions, such a requirement becomes unwieldy.

The credentials committee submits its recommendations to either approve or reject an applicant for appointment and privileges to the medical executive committee. In a well-functioning institution, the executive committee does not redo the work of the credentials committee but does make sure that the committee has done its work objectively and completely and that its recommendation is consistent with the information known about the individual. In rare instances, the medical executive committee's recommendation to the governing board will be different from the one submitted to it by the credentials committee. The difference may result from information being submitted to the executive committee that is different from that submitted to the credentials committee, a different perspective being brought to the applicant's credentials by the members of the executive committee, or a determination by the executive committee that the credentials committee's evaluation was not objective or complete. The executive committee may either ask the credentials committee to reconsider its recommendation or simply modify the recommendation before sending it on to the governing board.

The governing body has the authority and responsibility to make a decision on the application. It may either accept the medical executive committee's recommendation, accept it in a modified form, reject it, or ask the committee to reconsider. Because most boards are composed primarily of laypersons, they depend on committees of the medical staff for a professional appraisal of an applicant's ability to conform to the standard of practice established by the board for the institution. Thus, the board's primary role in considering a recommendation is to make certain that the approved procedures were followed and that the decision is made and communicated to the applicant in a timely fashion.

Liability Issues

If proper procedures are followed, the board and all medical staff committee members and hospital employees are better insulated from liability to their various constituencies. The board has a legal duty to the hospital's patients to use reasonable care in evaluating the competency of physicians who wish to use the hospital's facilities.[5] The board cannot guarantee that a physician will perform competently in every patient encounter in the facility; it can only exercise its duty to ensure that all reasonably available information about the physician was gathered and evaluated by the physician's peers and that a reasonable judgment was made on the basis of that evaluation. The issue in a suit alleging negligent credentialing is whether the hospital exercised that degree of care to be expected of hospitals similarly situated in evaluating the credentials of medical staff applicants.[6]

The members of the medical staff serving on committees that act on the credentials of applicants and reapplicants may be liable for conspiring to restrain trade if the board does not adopt proper credentialing procedures and then monitor to make certain that the procedures are followed. The issue of whether members of the medical staff are agents of the hospital when they do peer review and so cannot conspire with it, or whether they are individual competitors and are able to conspire with each other and the hospital to restrain trade, has been much debated in the federal courts. Some courts find that the medical staff as a group cannot conspire with the hospital but that physicians on the staff can conspire with each other in restraining trade.[7] Others believe that when the medical staff is engaging in credentialing and peer review, it cannot conspire with the hospital because the medical staff is "indistinct" from the hospital.[8] In *Oksanen v. Page Memorial Hospital*, the court expressed the most significant point for hospital boards to be aware of: ". . . where, as here, the peer review process has been operating in accordance with proper procedures, under the aegis of the hospital, and with a substantial basis in the evidence, the likelihood of an antitrust conspiracy is also substantially diminished."[9]

Conclusion

The hospital's governing board is responsible for monitoring and ensuring the competency of physicians who provide medical care to the institution's patients. Composed primarily of laypersons from the community, the board carries out this responsibility by considering recommendations made by the medical staff committees. The function of the credentials committee is to determine what the criteria should be for credentials in the various disciplines and then to apply membership and credentialing standards to applicants and reapplicants for medical staff credentials and privileges.

In evaluating applicants and reapplicants, the credentials committee works with the hospital's administration and its various medical departments and services to obtain data on applicants. In addition, the committee seeks information from quality assurance and utilization review committees in evaluating a physician's competence and professionalism. If all of these procedures are followed, the board and the hospital's medical staff should be insulated from liability and the hospital can meet its obligation to its patients and the community.

References

1. The Joint Commission on Accreditation of Healthcare Organizations. *Accreditation Manual for Hospitals*. Oakbrook Terrace, IL: JCAHO, 1992, p. 27.

2. Johnson v. Misericordia Community Hospital, 302 N.W.2d 174–175 (Wisc. 1981).

3. Ibid., at 175.

4. Ibid., at 175.

5. Ibid.

6. Ibid., at 171.

7. Weiss v. New York Hospital, 745 F.2d 786 (ed Cir 1984), *cert. denied*, 470 U.S. 1060 (1985).

8. Oksanen v. Page Memorial Hospital, 945 F.2d 696 (4th Cir. 1991), 703.

9. Ibid., at 707.

4 Overview of the Credentialing Process

Introduction

The relationship between physicians and hospitals is unique. Physicians generally are neither owners nor employees of hospitals; they use the facility but have no formal financial stake in its welfare and, some say, no loyalty to a particular institution. Physicians admit their patients to hospital beds, rely on the hospital's nursing staff to carry out their orders, use hospital equipment to diagnose and treat patients, and depend on the hospital's lab, pharmacy, and X-ray facilities, all without its costing them anything. Hospitals have been termed "the physician's workshop." Until *Darling v. Charleston Community Memorial Hospital*,[1] hospitals allowed all physicians who wished to admit and care for patients without concerning themselves with the quality of physician practice within the institution. However, the advent of Medicare and Medicaid meant that the government became a payer for health care services, and there was increasing scrutiny not only of the quality of physician practice, but also of the increasing cost.

This chapter discusses who must be credentialed and describes the different categories of physician and nonphysician practitioners. It also discusses the appointment and reappointment processes, and looks at the reasons why initial applications and reapplications for appointment may be denied.

Who Must Be Credentialed

The credentialing process is similar to the process that job applicants go through when they submit résumés and references to a potential employer and participate in personal interviews. However, because physicians and dentists are independent practitioners, most do not go through an employment process when they wish to practice at a particular facility. The hospital uses the credentialing process to ensure that all independent practitioners have the appropriate qualifications to perform the clinical procedures that are being applied for and the ability to cooperate with colleagues and hospital staff and to follow the institution's rules.

Even with respect to salaried physicians, a credentialing process takes place akin to that used with independent practitioners. The difference is that the overlay of employment law for those physicians who are employed by the hospital. Independent practitioners with a limited scope of practice such as midwives or certified registered nurse anesthetists (CRNAs), may practice in a hospital but they first must be credentialed. If the hospital allows physicians to bring their own employees to assist them in surgery, it must make certain that the medical staff bylaws provide a credentialing process for these assistants. Another example—if a psychiatrist employs a social worker or psychologist to make rounds in the hospital, because this person is employed by the physician and not the hospital and because this person has patient contact and documents the patient's chart, he or she must be credentialed by the hospital.

Categories of Membership

The hospital's medical staff generally divides its membership into categories. The category that a physician fits in affects the privileges granted and the physician's rights and responsibilities as a member of the medical staff. These rights and responsibilities include having voting privileges, being able to hold office, satisfying requirements to attend meetings, serving on committees, and taking call for hospital patients who do not have an attending physician or who require a specialist. There may be a category of physicians whose initial application has been approved that reflects the new member's probationary status. There also may be a category of physicians who have "courtesy" privileges, that is, physicians who want to be on the staff but who seldom admit or attend patients. Physicians in this category generally do not have voting or office-holding privileges on the medical staff. Active or attending physicians generally are those who have been on the staff for a specified number of years, have voting privileges, must meet specific meeting requirements, may hold office, and must admit or attend a minimum number of patients each year. Additionally, there may be an emeritus category of long-time staff members who are retired and no longer admit or attend patients.

Often, hospitals grant temporary privileges to applicants before the initial appointment process is complete. Either the applicant has not yet submitted a completed application or the process of approving the applicant for initial appointment and granting privileges is so lengthy that neither the hospital nor the applicant wants to wait for it to be completed in order to begin admitting patients. The hospital that allows an applicant to treat patients before the application for appointment and privileges is complete is gambling that the applicant can competently treat patients. If the hospital is wrong, patients will suffer and the hospital can be found liable for negligent credentialing. Such practices subvert the credentialing process. To protect patients, the hospital should make it clear to all applicants that they may not admit or treat patients in the hospital without having an initial appointment and having been granted the appropriate privileges.

An applicant for appointment or reappointment will apply not only for specific privileges, but also for a specific category. The applicant must meet all the criteria for being granted privileges in that category, such as the minimum number of admissions per year, length of time on the staff, willingness to take call and serve on committees.

Categories of Allied Nonphysician Practitioners

There may be specific categories within the medical staff for health practitioners who are not physicians and are not employed by the hospital, but who perform specific treatments or tasks for patients. For example, if the hospital allows physicians to bring in their own employees to assist them, the medical staff bylaws must provide a credentialing process for these assistants. The hospital may allow a surgeon to bring in a surgical assistant rather than use a hospital employee, but the hospital must first must credential the surgical assistant. The assistant must submit information required by the medical staff for such practitioners and must be credentialed through the medical staff credentialing process. Figure 4-1 shows a sample form for credentialing allied health practitioners or staff affiliates (or whatever terminology the hospital chooses).

In those states where podiatrists and psychologists are not required by law to be part of the medical staff and the medical staff has excluded them from full membership,

Figure 4-1.   Application for Clinical Privileges as a Staff Affiliate

Date

| Last Name | First Name | Middle Name | Degree |

Appointing Department   Division

Scope of Practice at ABC Hospital

Current Employer

Intended Supervisor(s) at ABC Hospital

1. **Office Location(s)**

   Medical Center Address (if any)   Mail Location   Office Telephone Number

   Office Address

   City   State   Zip Code   Office Telephone Number

2. **Identifying Information**

   Male _____   Female _____

   Social Security Number

   Home Street Address

   City   State   Zip Code   Home Telephone Number

3. **Licensure/Registration**
   Licenses or Certificates for Practice:

   Type   State   License No.   Date Issued or Renewed

   Type   State   License No.   Date Issued or Renewed

   Type   State   License No.   Date Issued or Renewed

   Please submit a copy of your current license or certificate.

4. **Educational Data**

   Undergraduate College or University   Degree   Graduation Date

   Street Address   City   State   Zip Code

   Graduate or Professional School   Degree   Graduation Date

   Street Address   City   State   Zip Code

   Please submit a copy of your diploma.

(Continued on next page)

Figure 4-1. (Continued)

5. **Clinical Training**

Type of Training	Inclusive Dates		
Institution	Name of Supervisor		
Street Address	City	State	Zip Code
Type of Training	Inclusive Dates		
Institution	Name of Supervisor		
Street Address	City	State	Zip Code

6. **Postgraduate Education**—Internship, residency, fellowship, preceptorship, teaching appointment or equivalent positions. Please provide information in chronological order and account for all time since graduation from professional or graduate school.

Position	Department and Specialty	Inclusive Dates	
Institution	Name of Supervisor		
Street Address	City	State	Zip Code
Position	Department and Specialty	Inclusive Dates	
Institution	Name of Supervisor		
Street Address	City	State	Zip Code

7. **Continuing Education**—Please attach a list of the types of continuing education activities you have participated in during the past 24 months.

8. **Membership in Professional Societies**—Please list current memberships.

9. **Professional References**

List three professional references who have personal knowledge of your current clinical ability, ethical character, health status, and ability to work well with others. One such reference must be the individual with the most recent organizational responsibility for your performance.

Name	Title	Telephone Number	
Address	City	State	Zip Code
Name	Title	Telephone Number	
Address	City	State	Zip Code
Name	Title	Telephone Number	
Address	City	State	Zip Code

Figure 4-1. (Continued)

10. **Institutional Affiliations**

List in chronological order all institutional affiliations including all hospitals in which you served in a professional capacity.

Institution	Category of Appointment	Inclusive Dates		
Street Address		City	State	Zip Code
Institution	Category of Appointment	Inclusive Dates		
Street Address		City	State	Zip Code
Institution	Category of Appointment	Inclusive Dates		
Street Address		City	State	Zip Code
Institution	Category of Appointment	Inclusive Dates		
Street Address		City	State	Zip Code

11. **Professional Liability Insurance**

A. Physician Sponsor

List the malpractice insurance carrier or medical protective society providing liability coverage for your activity at ABC Hospital.

Carrier Name

Policy Number	Amount of Coverage	Effective Date	Expiration Date

**A certificate of insurance must be submitted with this application unless
you are covered by the ABC Hospital malpractice insurance program.**

1. Have any malpractice claims been filed against you in the last five years? Yes _____ No _____

2. Have any judgments been rendered against you or have any settlements been made on your behalf for professional liability cases, including lawsuits or claims, within the last five years? Yes _____ No _____

3. Has your malpractice insurance or membership in a protective society coverage ever been terminated by action of an insurance company? Yes _____ No _____

If YES, what company? _____

Date terminated

If the answer to any of the above questions is YES, please explain on a separate sheet. Statements regarding liability claims or settlements must include the following information: (1) Description of patient, (2) Brief history and chief complaints, (3) Procedures and treatments performed, along with hospital course, (4) Specific allegations of negligence, (5) Resolution of claim (pending, settled without payment, settled with payment and amount).

B. Applicant

List the malpractice insurance carrier or medical protective society providing liability coverage for your activity at ABC Hospital.

Carrier Name

Policy Number	Amount of Coverage	Effective Date	Expiration Date

**A certificate of insurance must be submitted with this application unless
you are covered by the ABC Hospital malpractice insurance program.**

(Continued on next page)

Figure 4-1.   (Continued)

1. Have any malpractice claims been filed against you in the last five years?   Yes _____ No _____

2. Have any judgments been rendered against you or have any settlements been made on your behalf for professional liability cases, including lawsuits or claims, within the last five years?   Yes _____ No _____

3. Has your malpractice insurance coverage ever been terminated by action of an insurance company?   Yes _____ No _____

   If YES, what company? _____

   Date terminated

   If the answer to any of the above questions is YES, please explain on a separate sheet. Statements regarding liability claims or settlements must include the following information: (1) Description of patient, (2) Brief history and chief complaints, (3) Procedures and treatments performed, along with hospital course, (4) Specific allegations of negligence, (5) Resolution of claim (pending, settled without payment, settled with payment and amount).

12. **Disciplinary Actions**

    Have you ever entered a plea of guilty to, or has there ever been a judicial finding of guilty to a felony?   Yes _____ No _____

    Have you ever entered a plea of guilty to, or has there ever been a judicial finding of guilty to, a misdemeanor involving moral turpitude or to a misdemeanor committed in the course of practice?   Yes _____ No _____

    Has any license or certificate of yours ever been denied, suspended, revoked, limited, or otherwise acted against?   Yes _____ No _____

    Has your membership in any local, state, provincial, or national professional organization ever been revoked, suspended, reduced, not renewed, or challenged?   Yes _____ No _____

    Have you ever been subject to disciplinary action in any professional organization?   Yes _____ No _____

    Have you ever been allowed to resign your position rather than face any charge or investigation on the part of the Medical Staff?   Yes _____ No _____

    Have you ever agreed to limit your clinical privileges in exchange for promise by an organization or entity not to initiate disciplinary action or to sanction you?   Yes _____ No _____

    Have your Staff Affiliate appointment and/or clinical privileges ever been denied, revoked, suspended, not renewed, or reduced?   Yes _____ No _____

    Have you ever entered into a consent agreement, entered a plea of guilty, or found guilty of fraud or abuse involving payment of health care claims by any health care payer or been sanctioned by any third-party payer of health care claims or professional review organization, governmental entity, or agency?   Yes _____ No _____

    If the answer to any of the above questions is YES, please explain on a separate sheet.

13. **Health Status**

    Do you presently have a physical or mental health condition that may affect your ability to exercise the clinical privileges requested or would require an accommodation in order for you to exercise the privileges requested safely and competently? To answer this question appropriately, please report any condition which is infectious, which affects motor skills, cognitive ability or judgment, or which may adversely affect your ability to care for patients or to interact appropriately with other caregivers.

    _____ Yes _____ No

    Regardless of how this question is answered, the application will be processed in the usual manner. If you have answered this question affirmatively and are found to be professionally qualified for medical staff appointment and the clinical privileges requested, you will be given an opportunity to meet with the Physician's Health Task Force to determine what accommodations are necessary to allow you to practice safely.

    Sponsoring Physician's and Applicant's Consent and Release

    In applying for appointment, reappointment or clinical privileges as a Staff Affiliate of ABC Hospital, we, the undersigned Staff Affiliate and Physician Sponsor, expressly accept these conditions during the processing and consideration of the application, regardless of whether or not the Staff Affiliate is granted appointment or clinical privileges:

    1. We release employees of ABC Hospital, the Hospital and its representatives, and any third parties, as defined in Article IV, Part A of the Medical Staff Bylaws, from any and all civil liability which might arise from any acts, communications, reports, recommendations or disclosures involving me concerning activities; including investigations, reviews, monitoring or evaluation, relating to my professional qualifications, credentials, clinical competence, clinical performance, character, mental or emotional stability, physical condition, ethics, behavior, or any other matter that might directly or indirectly have an effect on my competence, on patient care or on the orderly operation of the Hospital or any other hospital or health care facility, including otherwise privileged or confidential information. It is understood that the foregoing release from liability shall be limited to acts done or communications, reports, recommendations and disclosures made in good faith without malice.

Figure 4-1. (Continued)

2. Any act, communication, report, recommendation, or disclosure with respect to us, made in good faith and at the request of an authorized representative of the Hospital or any other hospital or health care facility anywhere at anytime for the purposes set forth in (1) above, shall be privileged to the fullest extent permitted by law. Such privileges shall extend to employees of the Hospital, the Hospital and its representatives, and to any third parties, as these terms are defined in Article IV, Part A of the Medical Staff Bylaws, who either supply or are supplied information and to any of the foregoing authorized to receive, release or act upon same.

3. The Hospital and its representatives are specifically authorized to consult with the appointees to the medical staffs of other hospitals or health care facilities or the management of such hospitals or facilities with which we are or have been associated, and with others who may have information bearing on our professional qualifications, credentials, clinical competence, character, mental or emotional stability, physical condition, ethics, behavior or any other matter, as well as to inspect all records and documents that may be material to such questions. We grant immunity to any and all hospitals, health care facilities, third parties, individuals, institutions, organizations or their representatives who in good faith supply oral or written information, records or documents to the Hospital in response to any inquiry emanating from the Hospital or its authorized representatives.

4. We understand and agree that we have the burden of producing adequate information for proper evaluation of the Staff Affiliate's professional qualifications, credentials, clinical competence, clinical performance, mental or emotional stability, physical condition, ethics, behavior or any other matter that might directly or indirectly have an effect on the Staff Affiliate's competence, performance, patient care or orderly operation of the Hospital and for resolving any reasonable doubts about such qualifications.

5. We acknowledge the obligation upon appointment to the Staff Affiliate Staff to provide continuous care and supervision to all patients within the Hospital for whom I have responsibility.

6. We agree to abide by all such Bylaws, Rules and Regulations of the Medical Staff and policies of the Hospital as shall be in force during the time of appointment as Staff Affiliate of the Medical Staff of the Hospital, and to any amendments thereto of which I have been duly notified. In addition, I agree to protect and keep confidential all personal or proprietary information or records that are stored manually or by electronic data processing.

7. We have received and read a copy of such Medical Staff Bylaws and Rules and Regulations of the Medical Staff as are in force at the time of application and we agree to be bound by the terms thereof in all matters relating to consideration of this application without regard to whether or not the Staff Affiliate is granted appointment and/or clinical privileges.

8. We have not requested privileges for any procedure for which the Staff Affiliate is not eligible or certified. Furthermore, we realize that certification or licensure does not necessarily qualify the Staff Affiliate to perform certain procedures. However, we believe that the Staff Affiliate is qualified to perform all procedures for which privileges have been requested.

9. If granted clinical privileges, we specifically agree to (1) refrain from fee splitting or other inducements relating to patient referral; (2) refrain from delegating responsibility for diagnoses or care of hospitalized patients to any other practitioner who is not qualified to undertake this responsibility or who is not adequately supervised; (3) refrain from deceiving patients as to the identity of any practitioner providing treatment or services; (4) seek consultation whenever necessary or required; and (5) abide by generally recognized ethical principles applicable to our respective profession.

10. We acknowledge that any misstatements or inaccuracies in or omissions from this application constitutes cause for denial of appointment or reappointment or cause for summary dismissal from the Medical Staff. All information submitted in the application is true to the best of our knowledge.

11. We are willing to appear for personal interviews in regard to this application.

Signature of Applicant

Date

Signature of Sponsoring Physician

Date

Enclosures Required

1. Photocopy of License or Certificate
2. Photocopy of Professional/Graduate Diploma
3. Certificate of Professional Liability Insurance
4. List of Continuing Education Activities
5. Delineation of Clinical Privileges signed by the Clinical Chief and Sponsoring Physician

---

Clinical Chief

Date

Credentials Committee Chairman

Date

Chief of Staff

Date

Board: Senior Vice President and Provost for Health Affairs

Date

Source: Adapted from a University of Cincinnati Hospital, Cincinnati, OH, form.

the medical staff may nevertheless wish to create a separate category to credential these practitioners. Additionally, some medical staffs credential nurse midwives, certified registered nurse anesthetists (CRNAs), and other nurse practitioners who practice in the hospital but are not employees. Those institutions with teaching programs or that use moonlighting residents to cover certain kinds of patients may have a special category for these practitioners and may limit the practitioners' activities and their rights and responsibilities as medical staff members. Figure 4-2 provides a sample form for credentialing psychologists, nurse midwives, podiatrists, and other practitioners who are not physicians.

The privilege of admitting patients is as much a privilege as that of performing surgery and must be requested on an application. Not all members of the active staff will be eligible to request admitting privileges. For example, the practice of pathology or anesthesiology involves patient care but does not involve attending patients.

Initial Appointment

The term *appointment* means that the applicant is admitted to membership on the hospital's medical staff. *Privileging* or *credentialing* is the process of examining an applicant's qualifications and determining which procedures the applicant is qualified to do. Practically speaking, appointment is of no use to a medical staff member without privileges.

Application for Appointment and Privileges

Most physicians apply for privileges at several hospitals within the geographic area of their practice. Each hospital where the physician submits an application for appointment and privileges must go through the process of requesting information about the applicant's education, training, experience, references, malpractice history and then must verify the accuracy of the information submitted. Unless the hospital uses a credentialing service, it relies on its own resources to do all the work. The credentialing process is a time-consuming and labor-intensive process for both the applicant and, particularly, the hospital.

Some hospitals charge physicians a fee for the service or require that a portion of the medical staff dues each physician pays cover the costs of credentialing. However, physicians resist subsidizing this service, and many hospitals find that they must simply absorb the cost.

To have a complete application, the hospital must receive a vast amount of information from the applicant's medical school, residency programs, supervising physicians, and other hospitals where the physician has had privileges. (See chapter 5 for a detailed discussion of the design and use of application forms.) Because each hospital must process so many applications each year and because each application is time-consuming, the hospital must place the burden on the individual seeking staff membership to ensure that the information is submitted in a timely fashion. The hospital also should require that the application be *complete*, that is, that all degrees, licenses, letters of reference, and so on have been received by the hospital *before* the application is processed. In some cases, the physician may be waiting for the hospital to process his or her application, and the hospital may not have started the process because it is waiting to receive all the information the physician has requested. Sometimes, the information submitted by the physician with the original application becomes out of date by the time either the hospital or the physician realizes that nothing has happened on the application. In such cases, because the hospital should not base a decision on information that is more than six months old, the physician may have to submit updated information in order to start the process again.

Figure 4-2. Application for Clinical Privileges as a Medical Associate

Medical Associate status is limited to Geneticists, Nurse Midwives, Podiatrists, Psychologists, and Radiation Physicists who have faculty appointments in the College of Medicine

Date

| Last Name | First Name | Middle Name | Degree |

Appointing Department   Division

Secondary Department (if any)   ABC College of Medicine Faculty Title

Scope of Practice at ABC Hospital

Designated Medical Staff Appointee to Generally Supervise Activities

1. **Office Location**

Medical Center Address (if any)   Mail Location   Office Telephone Number

Office Address

| City | State | Zip Code | Office Telephone Number |

2. **Identifying Information**

Male _____ Female _____

Social Security Number

Home Street Address

| City | State | Zip Code | Home Telephone Number |

3. **Licensure/Registration**
Licenses or Certificates for Practice (Specify Profession):

Type	State	License No.	Date Issued or Renewed
Type	State	License No.	Date Issued or Renewed
Type	State	License No.	Date Issued or Renewed

Please submit a copy of your current license or certificate.

4. **Educational Data**

| Undergraduate College or University | | Degree | Graduation Date |
| Street Address | City | State | Zip Code |

| Graduate or Professional School | | Degree | Graduation Date |
| Street Address | City | State | Zip Code |

Please submit a copy of your diploma.

(Continued on next page)

Figure 4-2. (Continued)

5. **Postgraduate Education**—Internship, residency, fellowship, preceptorship, teaching appointment or equivalent positions.

Position	Department and Specialty		Inclusive Dates	

Institution		Name of Supervisor		

Street Address		City	State	Zip Code

Position	Department and Specialty		Inclusive Dates	

Institution		Name of Supervisor		

Street Address		City	State	Zip Code

6. **Continuing Education**—Please attach a list of the types of continuing education activities you have participated in during the past 24 months.

7. **Membership in Professional Societies**—Please list current memberships.

8. **Professional References**

List three professional references who have personal knowledge of your current clinical ability, ethical character, health status, and ability to work well with others. One such reference must be the individual with the most recent organizational responsibility for your performance.

Name	Title		Telephone Number

Address		City	State	Zip Code

Name	Title		Telephone Number

Address		City	State	Zip Code

Name	Title		Telephone Number

Address		City	State	Zip Code

9. **Institutional Affiliations**

In chronological order please list current and previous institutional affiliations where you have been granted clinical privileges.

Institution	Category of Appointment		Inclusive Dates	

Street Address		City	State	Zip Code

Institution	Category of Appointment		Inclusive Dates	

Street Address		City	State	Zip Code

Figure 4-2.   (Continued)

Institution	Category of Appointment		Inclusive Dates	

Street Address		City	State	Zip Code

Institution	Category of Appointment		Inclusive Dates	

Street Address		City	State	Zip Code

10. **Professional Liability Insurance**
List the malpractice insurance carrier providing liability coverage for your activity at ABC Hospital.

Carrier Name

Policy Number	Amount of Coverage	Effective Date	Expiration Date

**A certificate of insurance must be submitted with this application unless
you are covered by the ABC Hospital malpractice insurance program.**

1. Have any malpractice claims been filed against you in the last five years?   Yes _____ No _____

2. Have any judgments been rendered against you or have any settlements been made on your behalf for
professional liability cases, including lawsuits or claims, within the last five years?   Yes _____ No _____

3. Has your malpractice insurance coverage ever been terminated by action of an insurance company?   Yes _____ No _____

    If YES, what company? _____

                                                                                Date terminated

If the answer to any of the above questions is YES, please explain on a separate sheet. Statements regarding liability claims or
settlements must include the following information: (1) Description of patient, (2) Brief history and chief complaints, (3) Procedures and
treatments performed, along with hospital course, (4) Specific allegations of negligence, (5) Resolution of claim (pending, settled
without payment, settled with payment and amount).

11. **Disciplinary Actions**
Have you ever entered a plea of guilty to, or has there ever been a judicial finding of guilty to a
felony?   Yes _____ No _____

Have you ever entered a plea of guilty to, or has there ever been a judicial finding of guilty to, a
misdemeanor involving moral turpitude or to a misdemeanor committed in the course of practice?   Yes _____ No _____

Has any license or certificate of yours ever been denied, suspended, revoked, limited, or otherwise
acted against?   Yes _____ No _____

Has your membership in any local, state, or national professional organization ever been revoked,
suspended, reduced, not renewed, or challenged?   Yes _____ No _____

Have you ever been subject to disciplinary action in any professional organization?   Yes _____ No _____

Have you ever been allowed to resign your position rather than face any charge or investigation on the
part of the Medical Staff?   Yes _____ No _____

Have you ever agreed to limit your clinical privileges in exchange for promise by an organization or
entity not to initiate disciplinary action or to sanction you?   Yes _____ No _____

Have your Medical Staff appointment and/or clinical privileges ever been denied, revoked, suspended,
not renewed, or reduced?   Yes _____ No _____

Have you ever entered into a consent agreement, entered a plea of guilty, or found guilty of fraud or
abuse involving payment of health care claims by any health care payer or been sanctioned by any
third-party payer of health care claims or professional review organization, governmental entity, or
agency?   Yes _____ No _____

If the answer to any of the above questions is YES, please explain on a separate sheet.

(Continued on next page)

Figure 4-2.   (Continued)

12. **Health Status**

Do you presently have a physical or mental health condition that may affect your ability to exercise the clinical privileges requested or would require an accommodation in order for you to exercise the privileges requested safely and competently? To answer this question appropriately, please report any condition which is infectious, which affects motor skills, cognitive ability or judgment, or which may adversely affect your ability to care for patients or to interact appropriately with other caregivers.

_____ Yes _____ No

Regardless of how this question is answered, the application will be processed in the usual manner. If you have answered this question affirmatively and are found to be professionally qualified for medical staff appointment and the clinical privileges requested, you will be given an opportunity to meet with the Physician's Health Task Force to determine what accommodations are necessary to allow you to practice safely.

Applicant's Consent and Release

In applying for appointment, reappointment or clinical privileges as a Medical Associate of the ABC Hospital, I expressly accept these conditions during the processing and consideration of my application, regardless of whether or not I am granted appointment or clinical privileges:

1. I release employees of ABC Hospital, the Hospital and its representatives, and any third parties, as defined in Article IV, Part A of the Medical Staff Bylaws, from any and all civil liability which might arise from any acts, communications, reports, recommendations or disclosures involving me concerning activities; including investigations, reviews, monitoring or evaluation, relating to my professional qualifications, credentials, clinical competence, clinical performance, character, mental or emotional stability, physical condition, ethics, behavior, or any other matter that might directly or indirectly have an effect on my competence, on patient care or on the orderly operation of the Hospital or any other hospital or health care facility, including otherwise privileged or confidential information. It is understood that the foregoing release from liability shall be limited to acts done or communications, reports, recommendations and disclosures made in good faith without malice.

2. Any act, communication, report, recommendation, or disclosure with respect to myself, made in good faith and at the request of an authorized representative of the Hospital or any other hospital or health care facility anywhere at anytime for the purposes set forth in (1) above, shall be privileged to the fullest extent permitted by law. Such privilege shall extend to employees of the Hospital, the Hospital and its representatives, and to any third parties, as these terms are defined in Article IV, Part A of the Medical Staff Bylaws, who either supply or are supplied information and to any of the foregoing authorized to receive, release or act upon same.

3. The Hospital and its representatives are specifically authorized to consult with the appointees to the medical staffs of other hospitals or health care facilities or the management of such hospitals or facilities with which I am or have been associated, and with others who may have information bearing on my professional qualifications, credentials, clinical competence, character, mental or emotional stability, physical condition, ethics, behavior or any other matter, as well as to inspect all records and documents that may be material to such questions. I grant immunity to any and all hospitals, health care facilities, third parties, individuals, institutions, organizations or their representatives who in good faith supply oral or written information, records or documents to the Hospital in response to any inquiry emanating from the Hospital or its authorized representatives.

4. I understand and agree that I have the burden of producing adequate information for proper evaluation of my professional qualifications, credentials, clinical competence, clinical performance, mental or emotional stability, physical condition, ethics, behavior or any other matter that might directly or indirectly have an effect on my competence, performance, patient care or orderly operation of the Hospital and for resolving any reasonable doubts about such qualifications.

5. I acknowledge my obligation upon appointment to the Medical Associate Staff to provide continuous care to all patients within the Hospital for whom I have responsibility.

6. I agree to abide by all such Bylaws, Rules and Regulations of the Medical Staff and policies of the Hospital as shall be in force during the time I am appointed as a Medical Associate of the Medical Staff of the Hospital, and to any amendments thereto of which I have been duly notified. In addition, I agree to protect and keep confidential all personal or proprietary information or records that are stored manually or by electronic data processing.

7. I agree to accept committee assignments and such other reasonable duties and responsibilities as shall be assigned to me by the Board and the Medical Staff.

8. I have received and read a copy of such Medical Bylaws and Rules and Regulations of the Medical Staff as are in force at the time of my application and I agree to be bound by the terms thereof in all matters relating to consideration of my application without regard to whether or not I am granted appointment as a Medical Associate and/or clinical privileges.

9. I have not requested privileges for any procedure for which I am not eligible or certified. Furthermore, I realize that certification by a Board does not necessarily qualify me to perform certain procedures. However, I believe that I am qualified to perform all procedures for which I have requested privileges.

10. If granted clinical privileges, I specifically agree to (1) refrain from fee splitting or other inducements relating to patient referral; (2) refrain from delegating responsibility for diagnoses or care of hospitalized patients to any other practitioner who is not qualified to undertake this responsibility or who is not adequately supervised; (3) refrain from deceiving patients as to the identity of any practitioner providing treatment or services; (4) seek consultation whenever necessary or required; and (5) abide by generally recognized ethical principles applicable to my profession.

11. I acknowledge that any misstatements or inaccuracies in or omissions from this application constitutes cause for denial of appointment or reappointment or cause for summary dismissal from the Medical Associate Staff. All information submitted by me in the application is true to the best of my knowledge.

12. I am willing to appear for personal interviews in regard to this application.

Figure 4-2.   (Continued)

Signature
_____

Enclosures Required

1. Photocopy of License or Certificate
2. Photocopy of Professional/Graduate Diploma
3. Certificate of Professional Liability Insurance

4. List of Continuing Education Activities
5. Delineation of Clinical Privileges signed by the Clinical Chief

Clinical Chief _____   Date _____

Credentials Committee Chairman _____   Date _____

Chief of Staff _____   Date _____

Board: Senior Vice President and Provost for Health Affairs _____   Date _____

Source: Adapted from a University of Cincinnati Hospital, Cincinnati, OH, form.

Data Bank Information

In addition to verifying the information about licensure, Drug Enforcement Agency (DEA) number, malpractice insurance, and so on, the hospital must request information from the National Practitioner Data Bank to determine whether any malpractice judgments and settlements or anything adverse to the physician's privileges has been reported. If the data bank submits anything that the physician has not already explained to the satisfaction of the credentials committee, the committee must request an explanation before it formulates its recommendation.

Delineation of Privileges Form

In addition to submitting an application for appointment to the medical staff, the initial applicant will likely be requested to submit a delineation of privileges form. This form will have been developed by the department or clinical service the physician hopes to become a member of and will ask what procedures the applicant plans to perform as a member of the hospital's staff. The form may have an extensive list of specific procedures and will ask the applicant to place a check mark next to the privileges being requested, or it may simply group procedures and ask the applicant to indicate whether the request is for the simplest procedures under level I, the more complicated procedures under level II (which includes level I privileges), or the most complicated procedures under level III (which also includes all the procedures listed under levels I and II).

The form also may represent a combination of the two approaches. The applicant may be able to apply for privileges under one level and only specified procedures under the next-higher level. Some clinical services, such as cardiac surgery, lend themselves to listing each procedure; others, such as obstetrics, lend themselves to grouping procedures. In large tertiary care hospitals, some kind of listing or grouping procedure is included for all clinical services. In smaller or less-specialized institutions, all applicants in some clinical services, such as family practice, may be approved for all procedures done in the hospital in that specialty. Figure 4-3 shows sample forms for delineation of privileges in surgery, neurology, environmental health, and neurosurgery, showing a combination of approaches.

Figure 4-3. Sample Forms for Delineation of Privileges

Sample Form 1

Delineation of Privileges
Department of Surgery

_____   _____
Name   Date

_____   _____
Faculty Title   Signature

Three categories of clinical privileges may be granted.

(1) Surgeons with this rating are expected to request consultation in all cases in which doubt exists as to the diagnosis, where expected improvement is not soon apparent, and when specialized therapeutic or diagnostic techniques are indicated.

(2) Surgeons with this rating are expected to have training and/or experience and/or competence on a level commensurate with that provided by full general surgical training (the broad field of general surgery), although not necessarily at the level of the subspecialist. Such surgeons may act as consultants to others and would be expected to request consultations: (a) when diagnosis and/or management remain in doubt over an unduly long time, especially in the presence of life-threatening illness, (b) when unexpected complications arise, and (c) when hazardous treatment procedures are contemplated.

(3) Surgeons with this training have the highest level of competence within a given field on a par with that considered appropriate for a subspecialist. They are qualified to act as consultants in their particular subspecialty and in general surgery, but should in turn request consultation when needed in other subspecialty fields.

Category Requested

1. _____

2. _____

3. _____

Certain diagnostic and therapeutic procedures are considered special procedures and may be performed only if individual authorization has been granted by the director of the department on recommendation from or after consultation with the director of the appropriate division.

General Surgery

Abdomen

_____ Abdominal perineal resection

_____ Appendectomy

_____ Culdoscopy, gastroscopy, peritoneoscopy

_____ Hernia repair—diaphragmatic

_____   —femoral

_____   —incisional

_____   —inguinal

_____   —umbilical

_____   —other

_____ Operations on biliary tract

_____ Gallbladder

_____ Gastrointestinal tract

_____ Pancreas

_____ Spleen

_____ Paracentesis

_____ Uterus

_____ Ovaries

_____ Kidneys

_____ Bladder

_____ Endoscopy

_____ Tubes

_____ Perineorrhaphy

Blood Vessels

_____ Anastomoses

_____ Aneurysmectomy

_____ Embolectomy

_____ Phlebectomy

Figure 4-3. (Continued)

Blood Vessels (continued)

_____ Thrombectomy

_____ Vein ligation

_____ Graft

_____ —venous

_____ —prosthetic

_____ Surgery of portal hypertension

Breasts

_____ Excision of cyst or tumor

_____ Incision and drainage of abscess

_____ Mastectomy—simple

_____ —radical

_____ Reconstructive

Lymph Channels and Nodes

_____ Biopsy

_____ Incision and drainage

_____ Excision

_____ Radical dissections

Skin and Subcutaneous

_____ Tissue—biopsy

_____ Burns

_____ Excision lesion—cyst, lipomata, polyps, etc.

_____ Graft—pedicle

_____ Tubular

_____ Incision and drainage

—abscessed, paronychia, etc.

—deep abscess, thyroglossal cyst, etc.

_____ Suture—uncomplicated wounds

_____ Reconstructive surgery

Thyroid

_____ Thyroidectomy

_____ Parathyroidectomy

_____ Radical neck dissection

Chest Surgery

_____ Cardiovascular surgery

_____ Drainage—closed

_____ —open

_____ Pulmonary resection

_____ Phrenic nerve surgery

_____ Scalenotomy

_____ Thoracentesis

_____ Thoracic—abdominal incision

_____ Major surgery

_____ Endoscopy

_____ Tracheostomy

Esophagus

_____ Any surgery

Plastic Surgery

_____ Acute and reconstructive hand trauma

_____ Burn reconstruction

_____ Head and neck tumor resection

_____ Cosmetic surgery

_____ Breast reconstruction

_____ Tumor and acquired disease of the hand

_____ Acute facial trauma

_____ Skin grafting

Rectal Surgery

_____ Anal fissure

_____ Fistula

_____ Anoscopy, proctoscopy, sigmoidoscopy

_____ Excision lesion—local malignant

_____ Hemorrhoidectomy—external, internal

_____ Incision and drainage

_____ Pilonidal cyst

_____ Rectal prolapse

Emergency Resuscitative Procedure

_____ All necessary surgical procedures to control life-threatening hemorrhage or establish an adequate airway, or support cardiorespiratory function during an emergency situation.

Neurosurgery

_____ Craniocerebral trauma

_____ Craniotomy

_____ Laminectomy

_____ Spinal injury

_____ Peripheral nerve surgery

_____ Stereotactic procedures

_____ Intervertebral disc removal

_____ Microsurgery

_____ Sympathectomy

_____ Shunts

_____ Congenital lesions of spine and skull

_____ Contrast diagnostic studies

Urological Surgery

_____ Circumcision

_____ Cystoscopy, urethroscopy

_____ Cystotomy

_____ Hydrocele

_____ Nephrectomy—partial

_____ —total

(Continued on next page)

Figure 4-3. (Continued)

Urological Surgery (continued)

_____ *Orchidectomy*

_____ *Plastic operations on kidney*

_____ *Prostatectomy*

_____ *Transurethral resection*

_____ *Ureteral surgery*

_____ *Urethrotomy—external*

_____ *—internal*

_____ *Varicocele*

_____ *All surgery involving kidneys,*
urethra, prostate,
seminal vesicles, external
genitalia, and adrenal glands

Orthopedic Surgery

_____ Amputations—simple
(fingers and toes)

_____ Amputations—major

_____ Drainage—bone

_____ Repair tendons—primary

_____ —secondary

_____ Tenotomy

_____ Wounds sufficient to result
in permanent disability or
death

_____ Hand surgery

_____ Skin grafts

_____ Biopsy and/or excision tumors

_____ Microsurgery of extremities,
nerve and artery

_____ Peripheral nerve

Approval

Date: _____ Department Director: _____

Source: Adapted from a University of Cincinnati Hospital, Cincinnati, OH, form.

Figure 4-3. (Continued)

Sample Form 2

Delineation of Privileges
Department of Neurology

_____   _____
Name   Date

_____   _____
Title   Signature

To be accredited as a neurologist, physicians must have the highest level of competence within the field on a par with that considered appropriate for the subspecialty. They are qualified to act as consultants in neurology, but should in turn request consultation when needed in other subspecialty fields.

Certain diagnostic and therapeutic procedures are considered special procedures and may be performed only if individual authorization has been granted by the director of the department on recommendation from, or after consultation with, the director of the appropriate division. These special procedures are listed below. Please check (✔) those procedures which you wish authorization to perform.

_____ Insertion of central venous catheter   _____ Thoracentesis   _____ Referral for CAT Scan
_____ Arterial puncture   _____ Emergency tracheotomy   _____ Needle muscle biopsy
_____ Arteriography   _____ Endotracheal intubation   _____ Open muscle biopsy
_____ Cut down for I.V.   _____ Pleural biopsy (needle)   _____ *Other*
_____ Lumbar puncture   _____ Electrocardiography interpretation   _____ _____
_____ Cisternal tap   _____ External cardiac massage   _____ _____
_____ Bone marrow aspiration   _____ Rx with radioisotopes (RAI)   _____ _____
_____ Insertion of nasogastric tube   _____ EEG interpretation   _____ _____

Approval

Date: _____ Department Director: _____

Source: Adapted from a University of Cincinnati Hospital, Cincinnati, OH, form.

Figure 4-3. (Continued)

Sample Form 3

Delineation of Privileges
Department of Environmental Health
Occupational Medicine

Name _____   Date _____

Title _____   Signature _____

A physician granted privileges as a specialist in occupational medicine must have the highest level of competence within the field on a par with that considered appropriate for the specialty. Such a physician is qualified to act as a consultant in occupational medicine but should in turn request consultation when needed in other specialty or subspecialty fields.

Please check (✓) those procedures which you wish authorization to perform.

_____ 1. The evaluation and care of patients with medical illnesses of occupational origin.
_____ 2. The diagnosis and treatment of acute and chronic intoxication of chemical origin affecting such organ systems as:

  _____ Pulmonary
  _____ Skin
  _____ Reproductive
  _____ Central nervous system
  _____ Other (describe) _____

_____ 3. The interpretation of laboratory analysis of biological specimens for identification and quantitation of toxic agents and/or their metabolites.
_____ 4. The diagnosis and treatment of acute and chronic illness from physical agent sources (radiation, noise, thermal stress, vibration, etc.).
_____ 5. The planning, development, and implementation of occupational health programs for industries and communities of work populations. The objective of such programs is to prevent illness and injury from occupational or other environmental sources.
_____ 6. The design and implementation of toxicology research programs to assess degree of hazard and determine safe levels of exposure to toxic agents; interpretation of toxicologic data.

Provide proficient diagnostic services as follows:

_____ 7. Pulmonary function testing
_____ 8. Thoracentesis
_____ 9. Pleural biopsy
_____ 10. Exercise testing
_____ 11. Bronchial challenge
_____ 12. Methacholine challenge
_____ 13. Electrocardiography interpretation
_____ 14. External cardiac massage
_____ 15. Skin biopsy
_____ 16. Cutaneous examination, sampling and culture for bacteria and fungi
_____ 17. Cutaneous vascular and sensory function testing
_____ 18. Cutaneous patch testing and photosensitivity testing

  Other

_____ _____
_____ _____
_____ _____

Approval

Date: _____ Department Director: _____

Source: Adapted from a University of Cincinnati Hospital, Cincinnati, OH, form.

(Continued on next page)

Figure 4-3. (Continued)

Sample Form 4

Delineation of Privileges
Department of Neurosurgery

Name _____   Date _____

Title _____   Signature _____

Clinical privileges are granted to neurosurgeons having the highest level of competence. They are qualified to act as consultants in their specialty and to perform all diagnostic and therapeutic procedures except any exclusions which are listed below. Acceptable special diagnostic and therapeutic procedures include:

_____ Sterotaxic surgery
_____ Microsurgery
_____ Laser surgery

Craniotomy

_____ Vascular disease
_____ Tumor
_____ Trauma
_____ Epilepsy
_____ Miscellaneous disorders

Spinal

_____ Trauma
_____ Tumor
_____ Disc rupture
_____ Vascular disorders
_____ Congenital lesions
_____ Miscellaneous disorders
_____ Shunts

Vascular surgery

_____ Extracranial
_____ Intracranial
_____ Peripheral nerve surgery
_____ Sympathetic nerve surgery

Diagnostic Studies

_____ Vascular
_____ Spinal
_____ Miscellaneous

Exclusions

_____
_____
_____

Emergency Resuscitative Procedure

_____ All necessary surgical procedures to control life-threatening hemorrhage or establish an adequate airway, or support cardiorespiratory function during an emergency situation.

Approval

Date: _____   Department Director: _____

Source: Adapted from a University of Cincinnati Hospital, Cincinnati, OH, form.

The national medical specialty boards develop lists of privileges delineations for their particular specialties as recommendations in order to aid hospitals and physicians with the credentialing process. The Department of Hospital Medical Staff Services of the American Medical Association compiles these lists of privileges delineations and makes them available to those who request such information.

The application form requires the physician to submit evidence of clinical competence for those procedures sought in the delineation of privileges request. Such evidence may include a listing or description of the number of such procedures performed prior to the application. The information the physician supplies will be evaluated against the standard established by the department and approved by the board so that the credentials committee can make a recommendation regarding whether the physician should be granted the privileges requested.

Physicians just completing residency programs have records of the number of procedures they performed during their residency, and the information is easy to supply. However, first-time applicants who have been in practice for a number of years at other hospitals may have to do some research in patient records to compile the information requested. Unless an applicant can demonstrate competency in performing a procedure, such as having safely completed the minimum number established by the department or clinical service, the hospital should not grant the applicant privileges for that procedure.

Letters of Reference and the Importance of Verification

Applicants also will be required to submit evidence of their ability to relate effectively to their peers, the hospital staff, and patients. Such evidence probably will come from letters of reference from colleagues, medical supervisors, and personnel at hospitals where the physician has had privileges in the past. These reference letters should not be relied on without verification. Someone from the hospital must contact the person writing the letter to ensure that he or she has not omitted important information or misrepresented the physician's actual skills for fear of being sued for what was said in the letter.

Denial of Appointment

There are circumstances in which a physician requesting appointment to the hospital's medical staff may be denied by the hospital's board. Typically, such a denial will be based on the physician's not having met the institution's standards. If the physician does not supply all the requested information within a reasonable length of time, the board should not act on the application, thereby avoiding a denial which may have to be reported to the data bank.

Failure to Meet the Institution's Standards

If the credentials committee believes that a physician does not meet the standards set by the hospital for membership and privileges, it will likely recommend to the board that the physician be denied staff membership and privileges. Private hospitals may apply whatever reasonable standards they wish for admission to their medical staffs, as long as the criteria are rationally related to the provision of high-quality patient care and are applied to all applicants equally. When the board believes that the applicant cannot meet the standard of care for the institution, it should deny the applicant an appointment. For example, if the physician has been involved in several malpractice lawsuits and cannot explain this involvement to the satisfaction of the credentials committee, the committee should recommend that the physician be denied appointment to the hospital's medical staff.

However, the fact of involvement in malpractice suits alone should not prevent a physician from being accepted as a member of the staff. For example, involvement in malpractice suits may be more easily explained in the case of an obstetrician who accepts a large number of high-risk cases than it would in the case of a physician whose practice is only for routine deliveries. Even physicians who have high-risk patients, however, must be able to explain to the credentials committee's satisfaction each malpractice suit reported so that the committee may make a rational judgment about the physician's ability to perform the requested procedures.

There may be other factors that the credentials committee takes into account in formulating a recommendation to deny a physician membership on the hospital's staff.

Those that are rationally related to safe patient care include a determination that the physician has failed to demonstrate clinical competence or that documentation of the physician's ability to work professionally with hospital staff and colleagues is lacking.

Some criteria are not reasonable and may not be used to deny membership on the hospital's staff. For example, a physician cannot be denied membership solely on the basis of his or her membership in an HMO that competes with physicians who are on the staff or because he or she holds particular religious or political views. The board of the institution must make the decision to grant membership and privileges, but since most boards are made up of nonphysicians, the credentials committee's recommendations are usually heavily relied on.

Failure to Complete the Required Documentation

In certain circumstances, the hospital may avoid granting privileges if the applicant has not submitted all the documentation required by the institution. For example, if the hospital requires that all applicants be board certified in order to be appointed, applicants without board certification, no matter how well qualified they may otherwise be, have not submitted all the documentation required. Rather than processing the application and ultimately denying the appointment, there are advantages to the institution simply not to consider such applications. It would be easier for the hospital to defend its action in court if the physician filed suit because the refusal to grant membership was based on the physician's failure to meet an objective criterion rather than on a subjective judgment by the physician's peers. The hospital is likely to prevail on the basis that the applicant who does not meet the minimum documentation requirements will not have his or her application put through the credentialing process.

When Denials Are Reported to the Data Bank

Whether the application is denied or is simply not considered is an important distinction to make for purposes of deciding what reports to make to the National Practitioner Data Bank. Physicians who are denied privileges by the board based on clinical competence, even if they are submitting applications for initial appointment, must be reported to the data bank. In the example of the physician who is not board certified but is applying to a hospital that requires board certification, it is a subtle but important difference to say that the hospital will not process the application rather than eventually deny the application for privileges on the same basis.

For example, Dr. Sheila X is making an initial application to General Hospital for an appointment to the staff in the department of obstetrics with level I clinical privileges. She has completed a residency in obstetrics and gynecology but has not taken the examination to be board certified in her specialty. Last year, the board of trustees of General Hospital set as a standard for appointment in obstetrics and gynecology a requirement that all new members of the staff be board certified. Her application is reviewed by the credentials committee, which recommends to the medical executive committee that her application be rejected based on her lack of board certification. The board acts on the recommendation of the executive committee and denies Dr. X's application. The denial is based on an investigation of Dr. X's clinical competence and must be reported to the data bank. Had Dr. X withdrawn her application at any time before a final determination, even 5 minutes before the board acted, there would have been no denial and nothing would have been reported to the data bank. Even if Dr. X had not withdrawn the application, a recommendation on the application would not have gone to the board for action since the application was never completed. There would be no denial and no report to the data bank.

A slightly different twist on the same example demonstrates what happens in the all-too-frequent scenario of a hospital's granting temporary privileges while it is processing a physician's initial application. In this case, Dr. X has submitted an initial application and is granted temporary privileges, anticipating final approval. She then withdraws her application when she realizes that it will be denied because she does not meet the standard. However, because she is "surrendering" her temporary privileges during an investigation, the action is reportable to the data bank.

Due Process Requirements for Denial of Membership

Denial of initial appointment to the medical staff may or may not entitle an applicant to a due process hearing under the medical staff bylaws, depending on what the bylaws say and the reason the applicant was denied. Lawyers disagree on whether an initial applicant is legally entitled to due process if the application is denied by the board. Some believe that because the applicant has not been granted privileges, the denial does not result in the applicant's being deprived of a property right. Others say that giving an initial applicant a fair hearing is an inexpensive way of preventing the applicant from being heard in court. The hospital's legal counsel knows what the courts in the institution's jurisdiction have said on this issue and should provide guidance in handling individual cases. In addition, legal counsel should be consulted when the bylaws are being written or revised with a view to documenting in writing the stand to be taken in such matters.

Appointment Different Than Requested

The board of the institution may approve a physician's appointment to the staff but, after considering the information submitted by the applicant, may make its own determination of the privileges the physician is to be granted and under what circumstances the physician may exercise those privileges. This determination must be based on the board's belief that safe patient care requires that the physician be granted privileges different from those requested. For example, if a board-certified gynecologist requests privileges to perform laparoscopic hysterectomies but cannot demonstrate to the satisfaction of the board that he or she has performed a minimum number of these procedures safely in the past, the board may grant privileges to do hysterectomies, but not laparoscopic hysterectomies.

Rather than simply denying the privileges requested, the board may instead approve an arrangement that is safe for patients and allows the physician to get the necessary experience for performing the procedure. In the previous example, the board may allow the physician first to assist with a certain number of procedures and then to do a certain number under supervision before being allowed to perform the operation without supervision. The board's action will be defensible if the approval is done in the interests of safe patient care and if there is sufficient documentation to substantiate the stand taken by the board.

Yet another way to protect patients is to approve privileges contingent upon the physician's getting additional training for a particular procedure. The board must assure itself that the course, if selected by the physician, is legitimate training for the procedure. A certificate issued by the training organization is not sufficient proof of adequate training. Someone in the clinical specialty or department should analyze the course content and make a recommendation on its adequacy. In addition, the physician should demonstrate clinical competency as measured against established criteria.

When the board approves privileges different from those requested by the applicant, the result may be that some privileges will be denied. As mentioned previously, when privileges are denied on the grounds of lack of clinical competence, the denial is reportable to the data bank. The initial applicant is better advised to withdraw the request for those particular privileges before the board acts. If this applicant has no privileges to surrender, the withdrawal is not a reportable event.

Reappointment

The Joint Commission on Accreditation of Healthcare Organizations (JCAHO) requires that each member of the hospital's medical staff be reappointed at least once every two years. Although the reappointment process is less extensive than the process for initial appointment, it is still time-consuming.

Reappointment Form

The applicant must submit a reappointment form with the requested licensure, professional liability insurance, and DEA information. Details will be sought about the physician's involvement in pending or closed malpractice litigation and professional disciplinary actions. In addition, the applicant must provide references from other facilities where he or she holds privileges so that the hospital considering the reappointment can find out what privileges the physician holds at other institutions and whether he or she has performed those procedures satisfactorily. This information is essential, especially for physicians on the hospital's courtesy staff whose primary practice is in another institution. The JCAHO encourages hospitals to send out inquiries to get this type of information. If the hospital discovers that the physician is seeking privileges that he or she has not been granted at other facilities, the institution may not be able to obtain enough information to verify whether the physician can competently perform the procedures requested.

As in the initial appointment, the credentials committee verifies that all the information supplied by the physician is correct. In addition, before recommending approval, the hospital will request information from the data bank regarding anything that has been reported in the interim since the last appointment. If something has been reported, the physician must be able to explain the event to the satisfaction of the board before reappointment can be approved.

Delineation of Privileges Form

In addition to the application for reappointment, the physician must submit the delineation of privileges form requesting the privileges he or she wants approval for during the coming appointment period. Before recommending that the requested privileges be approved, the credentials committee must examine the applicant's practice since his or her last appointment. This information can be supplied to the credentials committee by the clinical department's quality assessment committee or by some other mechanism that collects and analyzes such data. The credentials committee then examines the evidence of the physician's past practice for those procedures requested and formulates its recommendation to the board.

Denial of Reappointment

Because governing bodies of health care institutions are becoming increasingly aware of their oversight responsibilities for the quality of patient care, denials of reappointment are becoming more frequent. When the board's approval was simply a rubber stamp for the medical executive or credentials committee, physicians who seldom set foot in an institution were approved for its medical staff year after year. Now, most institutions require that physicians who are reappointed have a record that demonstrates to the board that they have been productive members of the staff. If a physician has not admitted patients to the facility in the past two years, the board has no such record on which to reappoint. Physicians who do not admit or care for patients in a facility, or who do not intend to do so fairly regularly, should be denied reappointment.

A second reason to deny reappointment is when a physician has ongoing competency or behavioral problems that cannot be remedied with additional training, monitoring, or other means. Rather than revoking the physician's privileges during the appointment term, the board may choose to deny reappointment. For example, a physician who continues to berate or harass the nursing staff or who otherwise continually disrupts the smooth functioning of the patient care team despite documented warnings from the department chair or medical executive committee should be denied reappointment based on his or her inability to maintain a professional demeanor. The physician's file should contain ample documentation of the behavior problems as well as the attempts the hospital made to correct the problems before denying the reappointment.

Denials of reappointment will invoke the fair hearing process of the medical staff bylaws. If the denial is for reasons of clinical incompetence, the action will be reportable to the National Practitioner Data Bank.

Reappointment Different Than Requested

Just as the board can approve privileges different from those requested by an initial applicant, it also can approve privileges different from those requested upon reappointment. Physicians must be thoughtful in deciding what privileges to apply for so that they do not inadvertently put themselves in a position that requires reporting to the data bank. In evaluating an application for reappointment and delineation of privileges, the credentials committee examines what procedures the physician has performed and the clinical outcomes of such interventions. In the past, physicians have been in the habit of simply reapplying for the privileges they have been granted in the prior cycle without considering whether they actually perform procedures permitted under those privileges. If they have not performed a particular procedure in the recent past but have requested privileges to do so, the credentials committee has no evidence of the physician's current clinical competence to perform the procedure. In such cases, the committee should not recommend granting the privileges requested. The board is not likely to approve the requested privileges, and the denial will then be reportable to the data bank. If the physician requests only the privileges for which there is evidence of current clinical competence, the privileges will not be denied and nothing will be reported to the data bank.

Privileges Actions

Just as it is the hospital board's responsibility to approve appointment, reappointment, and delineation of privileges, so it is the board's prerogative to take action on appointment and privileges if a physician demonstrates a lack of clinical competence and/or an inability to comply with rules and regulations, work with peers and hospital staff, or fulfill the requirements of "citizenship" imposed by the medical staff bylaws. An action taken against a physician should be suited to the problem identified, and the reporting requirements of the data bank must be considered.

Data Bank Reporting Requirements

Any action that is adverse to the physician's exercise of privileges and that is taken for reasons of clinical competence or inability to cooperate with the hospital's staff must be reported to the National Practitioner Data Bank. In many instances, the action may be to require the physician to complete additional education or training in a particular area. If the credentials committee or the medical staff executive committee believes that the additional education alone will be sufficient, no action adverse to the physician's privileges should be taken. If the physician can continue to exercise the privileges granted until the education requirement is completed, no report is required. However, if the physician's privileges for a particular procedure are suspended pending completion of the additional training, the report to the data bank is required when the period of suspension is longer than 30 days.

The imposition of monitoring works the same way. If the physician is required to be monitored in order to exercise privileges, the action must be reported. If the physician is free to exercise privileges whether monitored or not, no report is necessary. A physician who is required to have a coadmitting physician must be reported to the data bank because the action limits the privileges that were granted to the physician.

Fair Hearing Requirement

The medical staff bylaws should provide that the physician is entitled to a fair hearing before any action may be taken that limits privileges granted to the physician. Any action taken to suspend for more than 30 days, revoke, reduce, or restrict privileges is included as "limiting privileges." However, those actions that do not limit privileges should not entitle a physician to a due process hearing. Similarly, actions taken against a physician's privileges that are for some reason other than clinical competence or inability to cooperate with peers and other hospital staff should not entitle a physician to a due process hearing. These actions include suspensions for failure to attend the number of meetings specified in the bylaws or failure to complete records in a timely fashion.

There may be cases that fall into a grey zone for which legal advice should be obtained on the need to report privileges actions to the data bank. For example, suspensions based on incomplete record completion that have an impact on quality patient care may, in fact, trigger a reporting obligation.

Conclusion

The need for greater oversight of physician practice makes the credentialing function increasingly important and much more difficult. Hospitals today must apply standards in a strict manner when considering initial staff physician appointments and current staff physician reappointments to medical staff membership. This strict adherence to standards also applies to nonphysician practitioners such as nonstaff physician assistants, podiatrists, nurse midwives, and others.

As a result, hospitals are denying initial appointment and reappointment more frequently than they have in the past. Typically, denials are based on the hospital board's determination that a physician does not meet the institution's standards of competency to provide high-quality care to its patients or on a physician's inability to work with colleagues and hospital staff or to follow the institution's rules. Such denials must be reported to the National Practitioner Data Bank. However, in the event that applicants do not meet a specific criterion set by the board, for example, board certification, the board may decide not to consider the physician's application, which would avoid issuing a denial that would have to be reported to the data bank.

Reference

1. Darling v. Charleston Community Memorial Hospital, 33 Ill. 2d 326, 211 N.E2d 253 (1965), *cert. denied*, 383 U.S. 946 (1966).

PART 2 | Implementation of the Process

5 | The Initial Appointment Process

Introduction

The credentialing process takes place after the hospital has determined what services it will provide and whether all physicians who provide those services will be considered for staff membership or whether the hospital will limit the number of physicians required to perform those services. In making these determinations, the hospital must consider the number of beds in the facility, its level of professional and support staff, and its equipment requirements, as well as a number of other related factors. In addition, the ability of the hospital to sustain its services is a function of utilization and consumer demand, which, in a sense, is a vicious cycle in which consumer demand is driven in part by physician utilization of services provided by the hospital.

In some cases, health care executives and board members may be pressured by the community to open new services or to expand existing units. Pressure also may be applied by physicians wishing to expand the scope of their practice. Other factors that must be considered include the hospital's market share and the level of reimbursement. Counter-veiling pressures may also be exerted by managed care groups that want to either limit the number of procedures performed by physicians or reduce the reimbursement to health facilities in which these procedures are performed. Because of these and other pressures, hospitals are faced with making hard choices that both support the integrity of the institution and provide high-quality service to the community.

Screening physicians seeking staff privileges is a time-consuming and detailed process. It involves developing an application form (or a preapplication form in some institutions) for initial privileges, verifying information supplied by the applicant, checking various data sources on physician information, and contacting references supplied by the physician.

This chapter discusses how to design an application form appropriate for the hospital's needs and how to manage the verification process. It also describes the granting and rejection of initial privileges as well as the granting of privileges under special circumstances. A list of resources is provided at the end of this chapter that may be contacted for guidelines when designing an application form and setting up credentialing policies and procedures.

Preapplication Screening

Many hospitals use a preapplication screening process as a threshold mechanism to determine who is eligible for appointment to the medical staff. Eligibility criteria are drawn from the bylaws. The preapplication process usually includes an informative letter or form that outlines the requirements for appointment. This letter describes the credentialing process and what the applicant must do to demonstrate his or her eligibility.

Preapplication screening serves many functions. It eliminates those physicians who are ineligible for appointment to the medical staff. In doing so, it reduces staff time that would otherwise be required to identify those who cannot complete the credentialing process. Moreover, it serves to deter those physicians who might apply for credentialing but would not likely complete the requirements. In essence, the preapplication process puts such individuals "on notice," and they can decide early on whether they want to take the time and incur the expense required to provide the documentary evidence needed to support an application for staff privileges.

The Application Form

There are a number of models available for the application form used to screen physicians seeking initial staff privileges. (One such example form is provided in figure 5-1.) Most health care facilities design their own forms, which take into account the legal requirements in the jurisdiction. The bottom line is that the document should pose appropriate questions and generate sufficient information that will enable the credentials committee to screen would-be members of the medical staff.

The questions on the application form should be clearly stated, leaving no room for interpretation by the applicant. Moreover, the questions posed should not violate applicable federal and state human rights and equal protection laws. Although on its face the Americans with Disability Act[1] applies only to establishments that meet or exceed a minimum number of employees, it has been suggested that the way in which *employee* is interpreted by the courts may result in the act's application to staff physicians.[2] If this is the case, the requirements set forth in this law also must be considered when developing an initial application form.

Some health facilities may be loathe to ask sensitive questions for fear of triggering claims of discrimination. Questions involving current drug or alcohol abuse, physical health status, and treatment for psychiatric illness are seen as particularly sensitive areas of consideration. (The Joint Commission on Accreditation of Healthcare Organizations [JCAHO], however, requires that the medical staff bylaws include a requirement that applicants for appointment and reappointment submit information on current health status.) Properly drafted questions can be developed to get at this information, especially when it is linked to essential job functions. The decision to grant membership and credentials should be made *before* there is any consideration of whether the applicant's health status requires accommodation. Because health facilities owe a duty of care to those to whom it provides care and treatment, due diligence must be exercised when screening would-be members of the medical staff. (See figure 5-1, question 15.)

The application form should provide the applicant with sufficient information to enable him or her to consider at the outset whether to actively pursue staff privileges at the institution. This information would include a description of what is involved in the credentialing process, a request for a designated number of references who can be contacted, the criteria used in evaluating applicants, and the documentation that should accompany the application. Instructions on the form should indicate that those applicants who have difficulty supplying written information should contact the medical staff office at the health facility for further clarification of the information required. The form also should include a clear statement that applications will not be considered until all information is complete.

Many health care facilities include a *release clause or document* as part of the initial application that must be signed by the applicant. The release indicates that the

Figure 5-1. Sample Application Form for Appointment to the Medical Staff

To Be Completed By Office of Clinical Affairs

Physician ID # _____

Temporary Privileges Given

From _____ To _____

_____
Date

_____
Last Name   First Name   Middle Name   Degree

_____
Appointing Department   Division

_____
Secondary Department (if any)   ABC College of Medicine Faculty Title

Scope of Practice at ABC Hospital

Medical Staff Category Requested:

_____ Attending: The Attending Staff shall consist of physicians and dentists who are in active clinical practice with full-time appointments to the faculty of the College of Medicine and who utilize the ABC Hospital as the principle site of hospital practice, actively participate in patient care and teaching programs, serve on committees, and participate in quality assurance, utilization review, department, Hospital and Medical Staff meetings.

_____ Active: The Active Staff shall consist of physicians and dentists who are faculty members of the College of Medicine, who meet the qualifications for appointment to the Medical Staff and who admit and otherwise use the ABC Hospital regularly. Active Staff are eligible to admit and attend patients, serve on Medical Staff committees and are expected, but not required, to attend department, committee or Medical Staff meetings. Active Staff are ineligible to vote on Medical Staff matters or hold Medical Staff office.

1. **Office Location(s)**

_____
Medical Center Address (if any)   Mail Location   Office Telephone Number

_____
Office Address

_____
City   State   Zip Code   Office Telephone Number

2. **Identifying Information**

Male _____ Female _____

_____
Social Security Number

_____
Home Street Address

_____
City   State   Zip Code   Home Telephone Number

3. **Licensure/Registration**

State Medical License Number _____ Expiration Date_____

Other State Medical Licenses (Past Five Years or Present)

_____
State   License No.   Date Issued or Renewed

_____
State   License No.   Date Issued or Renewed

_____
State   License No.   Date Issued or Renewed

DEA Registration Number _____

_____
                    Date Issued   Expiration Date

Please submit a copy of your state medical license and DEA registration.

(Continued on next page)

Figure 5-1.   (Continued)

4. **Certification**—Certification by Board, College or Equivalent. Does not refer to board-qualified or board-eligible status.

_____

Name   Date

_____

Name   Date

If not certified, give current status:

_____

5. **Premedical/Dental Education**

_____

College or University   Degree   Graduation Date

_____

Street Address   City   State   Zip Code

6. **Medical/Dental School**

_____

Medical/Dental School   Degree   Graduation Date

_____

Street Address   City   State   Zip Code

Please submit a copy of your diploma.

7. **Postgraduate Education**—Internship, residency, fellowship, preceptorship, teaching appointment or equivalent positions. Please provide information in chronological order and account for all time since graduation from professional school.

_____

Position   Department and Specialty   Inclusive Dates

_____

Institution   Name of Supervisor

_____

Street Address   City   State   Zip Code

_____

Position   Department and Specialty   Inclusive Dates

_____

Institution   Name of Supervisor

_____

Street Address   City   State   Zip Code

8. **Continuing Medical Education**—Please attach a list of the types of continuing education activities you have participated in during the past 24 months.

9. **Membership in Professional Societies**—Please list current memberships.

_____

_____

_____

10. **Membership and Fellowship in Specialty Organizations**

_____

Name of Organization   Inclusive Dates

_____

Street Address   City   State   Zip Code

_____

Name of Organization   Inclusive Dates

_____

Street Address   City   State   Zip Code

Figure 5-1. (Continued)

11. **Professional References**

List three physicians or dentists who have personal knowledge of your current clinical ability, ethical character, health status, and ability to work well with others. One such reference must be the individual with the most recent organizational responsibility for your performance, and one reference must be your Residency Program Director if you were a graduate in the last three years.

Name	Title	Telephone Number		
Address	City	State		Zip Code
Name	Title	Telephone Number		
Address	City	State		Zip Code
Name	Title	Telephone Number		
Address	City	State		Zip Code

12. **Hospital Affiliations**

List current and previous hospital affiliations in chronological order (present to past).

Name of Hospital	Category of Appointment	Inclusive Dates		
Street Address	City	State		Zip Code
Name of Hospital	Category of Appointment	Inclusive Dates		
Street Address	City	State		Zip Code
Name of Hospital	Category of Appointment	Inclusive Dates		
Street Address	City	State		Zip Code
Name of Hospital	Category of Appointment	Inclusive Dates		
Street Address	City	State		Zip Code

13. **Professional Liability Insurance**

List the malpractice insurance carrier providing liability coverage for your activity at the ABC Hospital. All members of the Medical Staff are required to have a minimum of 1 million per occurrence/1 million aggregate.

Carrier Name

Policy Number	Amount of Coverage	Effective Date	Expiration Date

**A certificate of insurance must be submitted with this application unless
you are covered by the ABC Hospital malpractice insurance program.**

1. Have any malpractice claims been filed against you in the last five years?   Yes _____ No _____

2. Have any judgments been rendered against you or have any settlements been made on your behalf for
   professional liability cases, including lawsuits or claims, within the last five years?   Yes _____ No _____

3. Has your malpractice insurance coverage ever been terminated by action of an insurance company?   Yes _____ No _____

   If YES, what company? _____

   Date terminated

If the answer to any of the above questions is YES, please explain on a separate sheet. Statements regarding liability claims or settlements must include the following information: (1) Description of patient, (2) Brief history and chief complaints, (3) procedures and treatments performed, along with hospital course, (4) Specific allegations of negligence, (5) Resolution of claim (pending, settled without payment, settled with payment and amount).

(Continued on next page)

Figure 5-1. (Continued)

14. Disciplinary Actions

Have you ever entered a plea of guilty to, or has there ever been a judicial finding of guilty to a felony? Yes _____ No _____

Have you ever entered a plea of guilty to, or has there ever been a judicial finding of guilty to, a misdemeanor involving moral turpitude or to a misdemeanor committed in the course of practice? Yes _____ No _____

Has any license or certificate of yours or your DEA number or its equivalent ever been denied, suspended, revoked, limited, or otherwise acted against? Yes _____ No _____

Has your membership in any local, state, or national professional organization ever been revoked, suspended, reduced, not renewed, or challenged? Yes _____ No _____

Have you ever been subject to disciplinary action in any professional organization? Yes _____ No _____

Have you ever been allowed to resign your position rather than face any charge or investigation on the part of the Medical Staff? Yes _____ No _____

Have you ever agreed to limit your clinical privileges in exchange for promise by an organization or entity not to initiate disciplinary action or to sanction you? Yes _____ No _____

Have your Medical Staff appointment and/or clinical privileges ever been denied, revoked, suspended, not renewed, or reduced other than automatic suspension of admitting privileges due to failure to complete medical records or due to poor quality medical records, at any health care facility? Yes _____ No _____

Have you ever entered into a consent agreement, entered a plea of guilty, or found guilty of fraud or abuse involving payment of health care claims by any health care payer or been sanctioned by any third party payer of health care claims or professional review organization, governmental entity, or agency? Yes _____ No _____

If the answer to any of the above questions is YES, please explain on a separate sheet.

15. Health Status

Do you have a physical or mental condition which could affect your ability to exercise the clinical privileges requested or would require an accommodation in order for you to exercise the privileges requested safely and competently? To answer this question appropriately, please report any condition which is infectious, which affects motor skills, cognitive ability of judgment, or which may adversely affect your ability to care for patients or to interact appropriately with other caregivers.

_____ Yes _____ No

Regardless of how this question is answered, the application will be processed in the usual manner. If you have answered this question affirmatively and are found to be professionally qualified for medical staff appointment and the clinical privileges requested, you will be given an opportunity to meet with the Physician's Health Task Force to determine what accommodations are necessary to allow you to practice safely.

Applicant's Consent and Release

In applying for appointment, reappointment or clinical privileges to the Medical Staff of ABC Hospital, I expressly accept these conditions during the processing and consideration of my application, regardless of whether or not I am granted appointment or clinical privileges:

1. I release employees of ABC Hospital, the Hospital and its representatives, and any third parties, as defined in Article IV, Part A of the Medical Staff Bylaws, from any and all civil liability which might arise from any acts, communications, reports, recommendations or disclosures involving me concerning activities; including investigations, reviews, monitoring or evaluation, relating to my professional qualifications, credentials, clinical competence, clinical performance, character, mental or emotional stability, physical condition, ethics, behavior, or any other matter that might directly or indirectly have an effect on my competence, on patient care or on the orderly operation of the Hospital or any other hospital or health care facility, including otherwise privileged or confidential information. It is understood that the foregoing release from liability shall be limited to acts done or communications, reports, recommendations and disclosures made in good faith without malice.

2. Any act, communication, report, recommendation, or disclosure with respect to myself, made in good faith and at the request of an authorized representative of the Hospital or any other hospital or health care facility anywhere at anytime for the purposes set forth in (1) above, shall be privileged to the fullest extent permitted by law. Such privileges shall extend to employees of the Hospital, the Hospital and its representatives, and to any third parties, as these terms are defined in Article IV, Part A of the Medical Staff Bylaws, who either supply or are supplied information and to any of the foregoing authorized to receive, release or act upon same.

3. The Hospital and its representatives are specifically authorized to consult with the appointees to the medical staffs of other hospitals or health care facilities or the management of such hospitals or facilities with which I am or have been associated, and with others who may have information bearing on my professional qualifications, credentials, clinical competence, character, mental or emotional stability, physical condition, ethics, behavior or any other matter, as well as to inspect all records and documents that may be material to such questions. I grant immunity to any and all hospitals, health care facilities, third parties, individuals, institutions, organizations or their representatives who in good faith supply oral or written information, records or documents to the Hospital in response to any inquiry emanating from the Hospital or its authorized representatives.

4. I understand and agree that I have the burden of producing adequate information for proper evaluation of my professional qualifications, credentials, clinical competence, clinical performance, mental or emotional stability, physical condition, ethics, behavior or any other matter that might directly or indirectly have an effect on my competence, performance, patient care or orderly operation of the Hospital and for resolving any reasonable doubts about such qualifications.

5. I acknowledge my obligation upon appointment to the Medical Staff to provide continuous care and supervision to all patients within the Hospital for whom I have responsibility.

Figure 5-1. (Continued)

6. I agree to abide by all such Bylaws, Rules and Regulations of the Medical Staff and policies of the Hospital as shall be in force during the time I am appointed to the Medical Staff of the Hospital, and to any amendments thereto of which I have been duly notified. In addition, I agree to protect and keep confidential all personal or proprietary information or records that are stored manually or by electronic data processing.

7. I agree to accept committee assignments and such other reasonable duties and responsibilities as shall be assigned to me by the Board and the Medical Staff.

8. I have received and read a copy of such Medical Staff Bylaws and Rules and Regulations of the Medical Staff as are in force at the time of my application and I agree to be bound by the terms thereof in all matters relating to consideration of my application without regard to whether or not I am granted appointment to the Medical Staff and/or clinical privileges.

9. I have not requested privileges for any procedure for which I am not eligible or certified. Furthermore, I realize that certification by a Board does not necessarily qualify me to perform certain procedures. However, I believe that I am qualified to perform all procedures for which I have requested privileges.

10. I acknowledge that any misstatements or inaccuracies in or omissions from this application constitutes cause for denial of appointment or reappointment or cause for summary dismissal from the Medical Staff. All information submitted by me in the application is true to the best of my knowledge.

11. I am willing to appear for personal interviews in regard to my application.

Signature _____

Enclosures Required

1. Photocopy of State Medical License
2. Photocopy of DEA Registration
3. Photocopy of Medical/Dental Diploma
4. Certificate of Professional Liability Insurance

5. List of Continuing Medical Education Activities
6. Delineation of Clinical Privileges signed by the Clinical Chief

Clinical Chief _____   Date _____

Credentials Committee Chairman _____   Date _____

Chief of Staff _____   Date _____

Board: Senior Vice President and Provost for Health Affairs _____   Date _____

Source: Adapted from a University of Cincinnati Hospital, Cincinnati, OH, form.

applicant agrees to the facility verifying information supplied in the application form and supporting documentation. The language usually indicates that the applicant grants permission to the health care facility to contact by letter and by telephone named references with a view to asking questions about his or her qualifications. The language often goes further, indicating that by signing the document the applicant agrees to the references providing confidential information.

A far more contentious variation includes language to the effect that:

... by signing the application form for initial privileges, the applicant agrees to refrain from bringing legal action against named references for providing information considered factual which in the absence of good faith or if made with malice would constitute defamation.

This type of clause is questionable for two important reasons. First, it really does not vary the law because false statements communicated to others that disparage the reputation or name of another are sufficient cause for litigation if made maliciously and without good faith. Such a lawsuit would be based on defamation. However, if a named reference in good faith provided an accurate, but nonetheless condemning profile of an applicant for staff privileges, there would be insufficient grounds for a defamation lawsuit. (See figure 5-2 for a sample medical staff appointment reference form.)

Second, lawyers disagree about the validity of clauses that attempt to waive the right of physicians to sue those who defame them. A waiver or release of this type might well be considered unconscionable and therefore not enforceable in law.

The better approach is to avoid the legalese in application forms. In lieu of such legalistic language, it is better to indicate that named references will be asked a series of questions about the applicant's ability to carry out the privileges requested at the health facility. By signing the application, the applicant acknowledges this fact.

Figure 5-2. Sample Medical Staff Appointment Reference Form

ABC Hospital
Medical Staff Appointment
Reference Form

Date: _____

Re: _____
(Applicant's name)

Name: _____

Address: _____

Dear: _____

Dr.: _____ has applied for (appointment/reappointment) to the medical staff of the ABC Hospital for privileges to perform _____.

The applicant has provided your name as a person who can provide a frank and complete reference in support of this application. It would be most appreciated if you would answer the following questions and return this form to the address noted above.

Please describe your relationship, if any, to the applicant. _____

How long have you known the applicant and in what capacity? _____

To your knowledge has the applicant ever been the focal point of complaints from professional colleagues, patients, nurses, or other health care personnel? If you indicate yes, please describe the nature of these complaints.

In the space provided below, please describe why you believe the applicant should or should not be appointed/reappointed to the medical staff of the ABC Hospital with privileges to perform _____.

I hereby agree that the information I have provided in this form is true and accurate.

_____   _____
Signature   Date

Prior to the implementation of an initial application form, it is useful to have it reviewed by a diverse group of individuals. Those responsible for human resources have particular expertise in avoiding the entanglements associated with human rights and equal opportunity laws. In addition, they can recommend specific individuals in state and federal government to whom the draft form can be sent for review and recommendations. Although having the imprimatur of such officials will not necessarily thwart would-be litigation based on discrimination emanating from the application, their feedback may shed light on areas of concern in the form that can be clarified and thereby reduce the risk of subsequent challenge.

The application form should also be reviewed by the health facility's forms committee and relevant medical staff committees. Once the form is in draft format, it is useful to field-test it to ensure that it generates the information needed by the credentials committee and others involved in screening initial applicants for staff privileges. If the form proves unwieldy or fails to produce the information needed, it should be revised and retested.

Before the application form is used for the first time, legal counsel should review it. If the hospital's lawyer is not expert in labor law issues, the document should be referred to someone who does have such expertise. The hospital's risk manager also can provide considerable assistance. Once the final format is prepared, the application form should be sent to the medical executive committee and the board of trustees for approval.

After the application form has been adopted, it should be reviewed periodically and updated accordingly. Input from those skilled in form redesign can expedite this process.

Getting the Right Information

The initial application for staff privileges should be designed to assist the credentials committee in answering some salient questions. For example: Is the applicant a trustworthy physician who understands the fiduciary obligation owed to patients? Does he or she possess the requisite training and skill to be granted the privileges requested? Does he or she enjoy a good reputation among his or her peers? Does he or she come well recommended by others in the profession?

The application form should be designed so that the credentials committee can obtain relevant answers to these questions. Questions on the form can be divided into logical blocks or segments. For example:

- Biographical information
  - Name
  - Address
  - Telephone number
  - Social Security number
  - Driver's license
- Education
  - Names and addresses of undergraduate schools attended and completed, including dates of attendance
  - Names and addresses of graduate schools attended and completed, including dates of attendance
  - Names and addresses of medical school completed and year of graduation
  - Names and addresses of postdoctoral training programs attended and completed, including dates of attendance and completion
  - Name and address of the health care facility where the applicant completed a medical internship program (the name of the supervisor and the year of completion should be noted)

—Name and address of the health care facility where the applicant completed a residency program (the name of the supervisor and the year of completion should be noted)
- Licensure and boards
  - List of states or provinces in which the applicant has a license to practice medicine
  - A list of states or provinces in which the applicant previously was licensed to practice medicine
  - An explanation of why the applicant is no longer licensed to practice medicine in those jurisdictions
  - An enumeration of board eligibility
  - An enumeration of board certification
  - An enumeration of Canadian, British, or other foreign medical specialty fellowships [R.C.P.C. (C), or R.C.P.C. in _____ specialty]
  - Current Drug Enforcement Agency (DEA) number, a requirement for any physician who prescribes controlled drugs (the DEA number must be renewed on a regular basis)
- Health facility affiliations
  - Names and addresses of hospitals where the applicant now holds staff privileges and a list of the privileges granted
  - Names and addresses of skilled nursing centers where the applicant now holds privileges and a list of the privileges granted
  - Names and addresses of home care agencies with whom the applicant holds staff privileges and a list of the privileges granted
  - Names and addresses of hospitals, skilled nursing centers, and home care agencies with whom the applicant held staff privileges and the reason he or she no longer does so
- Malpractice claims history
  - List of pending cases in which the applicant is a named defendant
  - List of situations in which the applicant has been notified that someone is contemplating naming the applicant as a defendant in a malpractice lawsuit
  - List of closed claims in which the applicant was a defendant and an explanation of the outcome of these matters
- Disciplinary actions
  - List of pending disciplinary actions against the applicant in any jurisdiction in which the applicant now practices or has practiced medicine
  - List of closed disciplinary actions against the applicant in any jurisdiction and the disposition of same
  - Criminal record (other than parking violations or related matters)
- Health issues
  - Inquire whether the applicant can perform the essential functions of the job with or without reasonable accommodation.
- Insurance
  - The amount of liability coverage the physician holds for malpractice
  - The type of policy (occurrence based or claims made)
- Privileges requested
  - Applicant's specification of the privileges requested
  - Applicant's request for temporary or locum tenens privileges in specified categories
- Performance thresholds
  - The number of procedures performed per year by the physician in the areas in which he or she seeks privileges (for example, if the physician wants obstetrical privileges, the number of cesarean sections he or she has performed on average over the past three years)

- The outcomes of these procedures
- Geographic location
  - The location of the physician's office or clinic and its proximity to the health care facility
  - The location of the physician's residence and its proximity to the health care facility

The application also should request supporting documentation that can be used to verify information supplied by the physician. This would include verified copies of current licenses and a verified certificate of graduation from the Educational Commission for Foreign Medical Graduates for foreign medical school graduates. A certificate of insurance for professional liability should also be requested.

The applicant also should account for all time periods from medical school graduation until the present. The application should indicate that the applicant will be asked to account for any unexplained gaps noted on the form.

Avoiding Questions That Should Not Be Asked

As indicated earlier in the chapter, there is considerable uncertainty about the application of the Americans with Disabilities Act (ADA) to credentialing of independent practitioners. Rather than run the risk of becoming the first "test case" to challenge the application of the ADA, many legal experts are advising their clients to take a very conservative approach. This is true even if it means running up against standards enunciated by the JCAHO with respect to the medical staff.

The net effect of this advice is to view the ADA and the interpretations of EEOC (Equal Employment Opportunity Commission) requirements as if this entire body of legislation, regulation, and case law applied to independent staff physicians. In essence, for purposes of federal antidiscrimination statutes, physicians are treated as if they are salaried employees.

The logical consequence of this position is to refrain from asking a number of questions that are deemed "suspect" in terms of antidiscrimination laws. This would include questions that result in identification of an applicant's gender, nationality, race, creed, sexual orientation, date of birth, religion, or ethic origin. Health facilities could find themselves in considerable difficulty if rejected applicants for staff privileges are able to prove that decisions were made on the basis of age, sex, race, or religious beliefs. Even though this may not have been the intent of these health facilities, there is much to overcome if the line of questioning and the results of the credentialing and privileging processes appear in any way discriminatory.

Perhaps the most contentious issue involves the limitations on so-called "health status" questions. Health care facilities face a difficult challenge, trying to balance their duty to safeguard the health and safety of patients on the one hand, and respecting the rights of the applicant for staff privileges. Many facilities have attempted to develop a "safe" question to as regarding health status. For example:

Please indicate whether you are able to perform the essential functions of the profession for which you are seeking privileges, with or without reasonable accommodation.

The key point is to avoid posing questions that are suspect. Moreover, as indicated in the discussion of verification of applications, practical steps can be take not to circumvent antidiscrimination laws, but rather to confirm that applicants for staff privileges have the requisite skills, competency, and other attributes necessary for a positive recommendation to the medical executive committee and board.

Apprising Applicants of Process

Applicants should be apprised of what will be done once the application is filed with the health facility. This should include a description of the verification process and the checks made with directors of internship, residency, and fellowship training programs. Applicants also should be informed that an assessment of their clinical performance during these programs will be requested. Similarly, applicants should know that information will be requested from department heads and the chief executive officer (CEO) of those hospitals in which the applicant holds or has held clinical privileges. The time frame for processing the application also should be made clear on the form. Moreover, as previously mentioned, the application should clearly indicate that an incomplete form or failure to supply required documentation will result in delays in the credentialing process.

Interpreting the Data

The information generated by the application form can provide the credentials committee with a detailed picture of the applicant. Although some may question the need to know geographic proximity to the hospital, others can appreciate it. For example, if the hospital is located in a part of the state that experiences severe snowstorms during the winter months, it may be difficult or impossible for a clinician living miles away to attend patients. By the same token, if the physician is on staff at a number of area hospitals and already has a busy practice, adding more operating room or clinic time might spread the physician "too thin" to provide an acceptable level of care to patients.

For some health care facilities, the critical point is not geographic proximity but, rather, the physician's ability to respond in a timely manner when called to attend a patient. If the physician cannot respond to a call to come to the health facility within a set period of time, it may be inappropriate to recommend that he or she be granted staff privileges. The rationale used to justify such a stance is the hospital's duty to provide high-quality care to its patients.

Performance thresholds also are valuable markers. If the physician is requesting privileges to perform high-risk procedures and has performed only a limited number of these interventions with mixed results, the credentials committee must seriously question the propriety of recommending that he or she be granted the request. However, if the physician has a strong track record of high-volume based on good outcome performance, the credentials committee would likely not hesitate to give a favorable recommendation based on this criterion.

The Verification Process

Verifying a physician's credentials can be a time-consuming process. Those responsible for the process need to be dogged in their pursuit of information that substantiates statements or information found in the initial privileges application.

Utilizing Verification Resources

In practice, verifying information requires documentary proof of education, training, board eligibility or certification, licensure, insurance, and other credentials the applicant claims to possess. For foreign graduates, the process also involves obtaining a notarized translation of diplomas or certificates. Additionally, the verification process requires contacting references for objective information on key points in the applicant's background.

Verification also requires accessing the National Practitioner Data Bank for information about the applicant. Official forms must be completed for this purpose and submitted to the data bank. A processing fee applies to individual queries of the data bank, and a contact person is usually designated by the hospital to communicate with the data bank. In some instances, this contact is an independent contractor acting as the agent of the health care facility in seeking information. That agent may be the state medical society. The fact that the data bank does not have a file on the physician is important, because it means that it has not received an adverse action report on the applicant.

There are other sources of information that should be explored in verifying credentials. One excellent resource is the Physician Board Action Data Bank operated by the Federation of State Medical Boards of the United States. The federation gets information from the state and provincial licensing bodies. As members of the federation, they supply data on a regular basis on physicians licensed or disciplined in their respective jurisdictions. Unlike the National Practitioner Data Bank, the federation also maintains information on physicians in Canada, a feature that may be important in contemplating a request for privileges for a physician who has been practicing in that country. Moreover, the scope of information maintained by the federation is quite broad, encompassing Medicare sanctions, consent orders, and denial and reinstatement of licenses, as well as revocations, probations, and suspensions. Much of the information is available to hospitals on a negotiated fee basis.

The tedious part of the process involves verifying information that is not easily obtained in writing. For example, it may be difficult to substantiate why a physician left the medical staff of another facility in which he or she held privileges. Was the physician forced to resign in a face-saving measure to avoid suspension or revocation of medical staff privileges? Similarly, it may be difficult for the hospital to substantiate malpractice claims information if the insurance carrier is reluctant to share such information.

Telephone or in-person discussions with department heads and CEOs of other hospitals can involve a degree of diplomacy in ferreting out salient information about an applicant's credentials. Department heads and CEOs may be loathe to commit to paper a negative profile of the physician. However, with skillful questioning, the astute investigator may learn important information that suggests that the credentials committee should not give a favorable recommendation on privileges. From a practical perspective, those involved in the credentialing verification process must learn to "read between the lines" of the applicant's responses as well as listen carefully to what is and what is not stated in discussions with others about applicants for staff privileges.

Adverse action reports on file with the National Practitioner Data Bank or a staff privileges suspension at another facility should be put in perspective. Negative information should serve only as a warning signal indicating that further investigation is necessary. Negative reports should not lead to the automatic conclusion that the physician is a "bad apple" to whom privileges should not be granted, although it should be made clear to physicians that negative information will be thoroughly investigated. Otherwise, physicians will be reluctant to provide such information.

Using a Verification Service

As noted in an earlier chapter, some health facilities find the verification process too time-consuming an enterprise to handle in-house. Thus, they use agents who complete the process on their behalf. Many local medical societies provide such a service. The American Medical Association also has created such a service called the National Physician Credentials Verification Service.® It uses a series of cross-checks to verify information supplied by physician subscribers to the program.

There are other services are available to fulfill this responsibility. The point is, however, that these services do not complete the initial credentialing process. Instead, these groups complete verification duties only.

The use of an outside group for this purpose is not without controversy. Although the process is quite complete and can save time, it does not necessarily get at the difficult areas of the credentialing process, such as telephone interviews with references or conversations with department heads at hospitals where the applicant has held staff privileges. Moreover, because these groups tend to follow a standardized format in their approach, it is unlikely that a uniform model will verify information not amenable to accessing data banks or other on-line information services. If this is the case, health facilities might want to use outside verification services as tools to augment their work rather than rely on them as their sole source for substantiating information supplied by applicants.

Discrepancies and Other Problem Situations

From a practical perspective, there are a number of risk factors that should serve as a warning to hospitals involved in verifying a physician's credentials. Because a physician has an identified risk factor does not mean that he or she should be rejected out of hand, but it does indicate that further information should be obtained before concluding that the physician possesses the requisite training, skill, clinical competence, or experience to be recommended for staff privileges.

There are a number of common risk factors. These include:

- A malpractice claims history
- Inconsistencies between the information provided on the application form and that supplied during the verification process
- Missing documentary information, such as letters of reference, written proof of board eligibility or certification, or the absence of a diploma from a foreign medical school
- An invalid DEA number
- Adverse action reports from the National Practitioner Data Bank
- Hospital disciplinary actions, Medicare sanctions, or license action indicated in a Physician Board Action Data Bank report
- Poor clinical performance data reported by other facilities in which the physician holds or has held privileges
- Poor recommendations from references, department heads, or CEOs of hospitals where the physician holds or has held privileges
- Revocation, suspension, or curtailment of staff privileges at another facility
- Unexplained time gaps between graduation from medical school and the time the applicant applies for staff privileges
- Lack of liability insurance coverage or cancellation of same
- Current documented alcohol or drug abuse problems for which the applicant has not completed successful rehabilitation (rehabilitated alcoholics and drug users are protected under the ADA, but unsuccessfully rehabilitated alcoholics and/or drug abusers are not)
- Patterns of frequently moving from one city or state to another with no obvious reason for leaving a well-established or successful medical practice

The applicant should be notified when such questions are found in the credentialing process. When notified of the problem, the applicant should be given the opportunity to correct these discrepancies. However, the applicant should be informed that failure to rectify the problem will result in a recommendation not to approve his or her application for staff privileges.

Notification of discrepancies or other problems should be made in writing. The letter or form should indicate in clear terms what is necessary to complete the application process. Relying on telephone discussions or in-person communications can be risky, because in the absence of documentation, the physician can claim that no one ever indicated that there were problems with his or her application.

Verbal assurances by the clinician whose application is being investigated should not be accepted in lieu of documentation. The physician's attempt to smooth over discrepancies in the application or supporting written evidence should be rejected. A consistent approach that requires all applicants to meet the same requirements in the initial credentialing process is the best approach. In this way it cannot be claimed that one physician was given preferential consideration over another.

The Granting of Initial Privileges

Once all the information has been collected and analyzed, a recommendation should be issued to accept or reject the physician's application for staff privileges. A positive recommendation should include a list of privileges to be approved for the physician and the reasons for the recommendation. By the same token, a recommendation to reject the application should be substantiated in writing.

Initial privileges usually are granted to a physician for a probationary period. During this probationary period, the physician must demonstrate adherence to medical staff bylaws and clinical standards. In many cases, this may mean performing a certain number of procedures within the probationary period or working under the supervision of another physician who holds full privileges in the same area or specialty.

There is a sound rationale for probationary status. Although the credentialing process provides a significant amount of information, it does not give the health care facility a firsthand opportunity to observe the physician's performance or ability. Granting privileges on a probationary basis accommodates the hospital's need for firsthand observation and at the same time permits the physician to treat patients as a member of the medical staff.

Supervision and evaluation are quite important during the probationary period. Hospitals must be specific in terms of what constitutes "supervision" and the types of reports required for the evaluation process. A full-fledged member of the medical staff who is several miles away at a private medical office cannot be said to supervise a probationary holder of privileges. The parameters of supervision should be clearly spelled out for the benefit of hospital personnel and the medical staff.

The firsthand observations of the supervising physician are critical to deciding whether it is appropriate to discontinue probationary status. This means that the supervising physician's observations must be accurate and convey salient information on a number of items, including:

- Proper pretreatment workup and documentation
- Proper technique
- Proper posttreatment care and documentation
- Appropriate medication orders
- Timely completion of patient records
- Adherence to hospital policy and procedures
- Outcomes within acceptable levels of performance
- Ability to handle complications, including consultation with other clinicians in appropriate situations

To ensure accuracy in the evaluation process, the criteria used should be uniform within a medical department. This may include use of department quality assurance or outcome data for the probationary clinician and the department's overall performance information. Prior to taking on their duties, both the probationary physician and the supervising physician should be apprised of the terms of reference for the evaluation process.

The length of time set for the probationary period may vary among medical specialty groups. The probationary period also may vary according to the number of procedures the physician must perform for a proper evaluation. This information also should be made known to the probationary physician.

Once the evaluation is completed, a determination can be made whether to terminate the probationary period. In some cases, the outcome may be to grant the physician full-privileges status. In other situations, it may require the physician to hone clinical skills as a prerequisite to consideration for such status. Regardless of the decision, the rationale for the determination should be consistent with the facility's policy on the topic and should be substantiated in writing.

Privileges Delineation in Special Circumstances

The bylaws should be specific about the credentialing requirements for granting privileges in special circumstances. This would include temporary privileges granted to a well-respected expert who is asked to participate in the management of a specific patient. It also would cover the issue of *locum tenens* and courtesy privileges.

Good recommendations from other physicians or a national reputation are not sufficient criteria for credentialing physicians for privileges in these special circumstances. As with other physicians who seek regular privileges delineation, they must be properly credentialed. To this end, there should be ample documentary evidence that these physicians possess the requisite education, training, skill, experience, and licensure to treat patients in the health care facility. Moreover, there must be documentary proof of professional liability insurance coverage.

Because these physicians are transient, it is likely that hospitals will impose firm restrictions on the scope of the work they can perform in the facility. From a risk management standpoint, this helps to lessen the prospect of liability exposure stemming from procedures that exceed the scope of skill or training of support staff. Such restrictions should be noted on the application form.

Although some medical staff members may find such a policy too restrictive, others are likely to give it high marks. Because a well-known physician or surgeon has impeccable credentials does not mean that the hospital can support his or her work on a visiting basis. The absence of necessary equipment and properly trained support personnel could have a negative impact on the patient's outcome.

As mentioned in chapter 4, some hospitals grant temporary privileges to physicians whose applications are in the midst of being processed. In essence, by granting the physician temporary privileges, the hospital is banking on a positive outcome from the credentialing review. What is not anticipated, however, is the risk of liability exposure for physicians who are involved in misadventures during this period. Because the hospital may be liable for injuries to patients that result from failure to complete a thorough credentials review, the hospital should consider limiting such risk exposure by discouraging the use of temporary privileges in such cases.

As discussed in chapter 2, there is another special circumstance that goes beyond the matter of courtesy or temporary privileges. This issue involves physicians who want to be credentialed in subspecialty areas claimed by more than one medical department. Because the departments cannot agree on credentialing criteria and they fear losing their market share, the situation is ripe for political turf wars within a hospital.

The issue is likely to emerge in hospitals that perform high-tech procedures or that have well-delineated medical staff privileges. Anticipating the problem can avoid the turf wars. A firm hand exercised by senior management and medical directors can help to facilitate a solution to the problem. Rather than having various departments duplicate each other's efforts in monitoring performance, a consistent approach can be used to address the problem. This includes credentialing criteria and a multidisciplinary approach evaluating whether a physician has the requisite qualifications to hold privileges in a shared subspecialty area.

Rejections of Initial Applications

State law should be examined closely to determine whether any legal requirements must be met when rejecting an initial applicant for staff privileges. Laws would likely focus on notice and information to substantiate the rejection.

Legal counsel also should be consulted on this matter. Where there are no state statutes or regulations on the topic, case law may provide guidance. The requirements of due process should be considered when handling the rejection of initial applicants for staff privileges.

Rather than take a haphazard approach, health facilities should develop policies and procedures for handling the rejection of initial applications. These policies and procedures should be geared toward preventing lawsuits based on wrongful denial of initial privileges. This means having a set process in place for evaluating applications and having in hand documentary proof that these requirements were followed in this situation.

A risk management approach can be useful, particularly one directed at preventing such litigation. Such an approach would encompass the following considerations:

1. A detailed process for evaluating an initial application
2. A detailed process for verifying information supplied by the applicant
3. A description of how the credentials committee is to reach its recommendation
4. A review of minutes of the meeting of the credentials committee to determine that the application evaluation process was consistent with policy and procedure
5. A notification of rejection that includes pertinent information, such as (a) who should speak with the applicant, (b) restrictions on what should be communicated verbally, and (c) a written explanation of the reasons for either rejecting the request for staff privileges or recommending a different type of privileges designation for the applicant
7. Requirements for granting temporary privileges to a highly trained expert or a locum tenens
8. Policy on maintaining confidentiality of information gathered in the credentialing process
9. Policy on recording information gathered during telephone conversations or in-person interviews in verifying details supplied by the applicant
10. Policy on record retention for the credentialing process, including the minutes of the credentials committee
11. Requirements for notifying the insurer when a claim is anticipated based on wrongful denial of initial staff privileges
12. Implementation of a "damage control" policy for situations that become the subject of media and community attention.

In addition to policies and procedures, a risk management approach would include educating those involved in the credentialing process. Practical training is important on a number of issues, including confidentiality, proper documentation techniques, and the process to follow when verifying information with third parties such as the

National Practitioner Data Bank. Training or in-service education should be included for those who serve on the credentials committee to ensure that they understand their mandate and the way that meetings should proceed.

Involving the risk manager in difficult cases should be contemplated in a program designed to avert wrongful denial of privileges actions. The same is true for legal counsel. The procedure for contacting these individuals and the scope of their mandate should be delineated.

Conclusion

Once the hospital has determined the services it wants to provide and the number of physicians required to provide them, it sets up a credentialing process. The first step of the process is to design an application form for physicians seeking privileges in the institution. A well-designed form will describe the credentialing process, request the applicant to provide a designated number of references, outline the criteria that will be used to evaluate the applicant, and describe the information to be provided by the applicant. The form also should explain to the applicant the consequences of not providing all the information requested.

Once the information requested on the application form has been collected and verified, the credentials committee is ready to make its recommendation on credentialing the applicant. If the committee recommends that initial privileges be granted, privileges typically are granted for a probationary period or may be granted in special circumstances, such as temporary privileges or locum tenens and courtesy privileges. If the committee recommends that privileges be denied, it should use a risk management approach to arrive at that decision, basing it on policies and procedures established by the hospital documenting the reasons for the determination, and on consultations with the hospital's attorney and/or risk manager.

References

1. 42 U.S.C. §§1211 to 12213 (1990).

2. Remarks of Mr. Eric Springer, Esq. at the American Society of Healthcare Risk Managers (ASHRM) annual meeting, Las Vegas, Nov. 1992.

Resources

Disability Rights Education and Defense Fund, Inc.
1616 P Street, NW, Suite 100
Washington, DC 20036
202/328-5185

Equal Employment Opportunity Commission
1801 L Street, NW
Washington, DC 20507
202/871-3362

Federation of State Medical Boards
2626-B West Freeway, Suite 200
Fort Worth, TX 76102
817/335-1141

National Physician Credentials Verification Service
American Medical Association
515 North State Street
Chicago, IL 60610
312/464-5000

National Practitioner Data Bank
P.O. Box 6050
Camarillo, CA 93011-6050
Help Line: 1-800/767-6732

Office on the Americans with Disabilities Act
U.S. Department of Justice, Civil Rights Division
P.O. Box 66118
Washington, DC 20035-6118
202/514-0301

6 | The Reappointment Process

Introduction

Traditionally in many hospitals, once the credentialing process took place and privileges were granted to initial applicants to the medical staff, there was no reappointment process. A physician's privileges were held as long as he or she wanted them, although there might be occasional changes from time to time. Unless something rather dramatic occurred, or unless a deterioration in performance was patently obvious, there was no system in place to trigger a review or reassessment of the physician's privileges.

Even when many hospitals granted privileges on a fixed-term basis, the review at the end of the fixed term was often superficial. In many hospitals, the physician holding the privileges did not even reapply for reappointment; it was considered automatic.

Today, such a practice is unacceptable. Medical staff privileges automatically come to an end, and to have them continue, the physician must reapply. As with an initial application, an application for reappointment must be assessed. The result of the assessment may be a recommendation to grant the privileges sought, to grant a modification of the privileges sought, or to deny the application for privileges.

The reappointment credentialing process begins with the receipt of the application. Many of the questions asked are the same as those that were posed when privileges were sought for the first time. (See figures 6-1 and 6-2 for sample reappointment forms.) The primary question to be answered in the credentialing process triggered by an application for reappointment is whether the applicant meets the standards required by the hospital to carry out the privileges sought in the application. As the reappointment process becomes restrictive, physicians must provide evidence of current clinical competence for the privileges they seek. If the candidate for reappointment cannot demonstrate having performed a minimum number of procedures for the privileges requested, the application is much more likely to be denied than it would have been in the past. Another question is whether the hospital has the facilities, staff, and equipment to support the privileges being sought.

The fact that these questions may have been asked at the time of the original application does not negate the necessity for asking again at the time of reappointment. Because circumstances may have changed, it should not be assumed that the applicant's answers will be the same.

This chapter discusses the criteria, both objective and subjective, on which the physician seeking reappointment is to be evaluated. It also discusses the proper use of quality review data and health assessment information in the credentialing process and how to handle the rejection of reappointment applications or the curtailment of specific privileges.

Figure 6-1. Sample Reappointment Form 1

Reappointment Application
Medical Staff

I. **Basic Data**

_____
Name

_____
Office Address

_____
Telephone No.   Fax No.

_____
Home Address

_____
Telephone No.   Social Security No.

II. **Privileges Appointment Information**

Department(s) in which applicant currently holds appointment(s):

				Change Requested	
Primary Appointment:	**Cross-Appointment:**	**Delineated Privileges Granted:**	**Expiration Date:**	**Yes**	**No**
_____	_____	_____	_____	—	—
_____	_____	_____	_____	—	—
_____	_____	_____	_____	—	—

Please indicate in detail the nature of the change (deletion/addition) requested:

_____
_____
_____

III. **Status Update Information**

If you answer yes to any of the following questions, please provide a detailed explanation on a separate piece of paper. Make certain to number the separate sheet(s) of paper to correspond to the question being answered.

Since your last appointment: **Yes No**

1. Have you had any change(s) in your license to practice in any state? — —
2. Have you been charged or convicted of any misdemeanor or felony charge? — —
3. Has your narcotics registration certificate been called into question, suspended, or revoked? — —
4. Have you been the subject of professional disciplinary charges, hearings, or dispositions in state(s) in which you are licensed to practice? — —
5. Have you been granted staff privileges at any other health facilities? If so, please provide the name(s) and address(es) of these facilities and privileges granted. — —
6. Have you been the subject of staff privileges inquiries or action at any other facilities? — —
7. Have you taken or been granted a leave of absence with respect to your medical staff privileges at any health facility? — —
8. Have you voluntarily resigned from the medical staff of a health care facility? — —
9. Have your privileges been curtailed, suspended, revoked, or changed at any health care facility? — —
10. Has your specialty board status changed? — —
11. Please indicate whether you are able to perform the essential functions of the profession for which you are seeking privileges with or without reasonable accommodation. — —

IV. **Liability Insurance and Malpractice Information**

If you answer yes to any of the following questions, please provide a detailed explanation on a separate piece of paper. Make certain to number the separate sheet(s) of paper to correspond to the question being answered. Include the name and docket number of the case, the nature of the claim, the judgment, and damages awarded.

Figure 6-1. (Continued)

	Yes	No

12. Have you changed professional liability insurance carriers and/or the extent of liability insurance coverage since your last appointment to the medical staff? ___ ___

13. Have you been named as a party in any professional liability lawsuits since you last applied for appointment to the medical staff? ___ ___

14. Have you or your professional corporation been involved in any settlements or judgments of professional liability lawsuits since you last applied for appointment to the medical staff? ___ ___

15. Since your last appointment to the medical staff, has your professional liability carrier excluded any practices or procedures from stated coverage? ___ ___

All applications are to be accompanied by a certificate of insurance.
Photocopies will not be accepted.

V. **Medical Staff Responsibilities**

State the number of hours of continuing medical education completed since your last application for appointment to the medical staff _____.

In the space provided, indicate the medical staff committees you served as a member since your last application for appointment to the medical staff and the number of meetings you attended.

Committees: Meetings Attended:

_____   _____

_____   _____

_____   _____

Since your last application for appointment to the medical staff, have you been suspended, sanctioned, or warned about incomplete patient records? If the answer is yes, please provide a brief explanation including the date(s) and detail(s) of the action taken regarding incomplete records.

_____

_____

_____

_____

_____

_____

If your current delineated privileges are based on a minimum threshold of procedures to be performed per calendar year (for example, routine deliveries, cardiac catheterizations, mammograms, and so on), please complete the following:

Delineated Privilege(s)	Minimum Number of Procedures Required To Be Performed	Number Completed	(Outcome[s] Information Will Be Obtained from Department Chairman)
_____	_____	_____	
_____	_____	_____	
_____	_____	_____	

> The information furnished in this application and accompanying documentation is true and accurate. I understand that any misrepresentation or inaccuracy may serve as the basis for an automatic rejection of my application for reappointment to the medical staff. By signing this application, I hereby authorize the release of any and all information deemed necessary for a complete evaluation of my qualifications for reappointment to the medical staff. I hereby authorize the chairman of my department and those listed as references to provided candid and accurate information necessary to facilitate a thorough review of my application for reappointment to the medical staff.

On a separate sheet of paper, list the name(s) and address(es) of three individuals who have agreed to serve as references for your reappointment to the medical staff. Have each reference complete the reference form.

_____   _____
Applicant's Signature   Date

Figure 6-2.   Sample Reappointment Form 2

_____

                                                    Date

_____

Last Name   First Name   Middle Name   Degree

_____

Appointing Department   Division

_____

Secondary Department (if any)   College of Medicine Faculty Title

_____

Scope of Practice at ABC Hospital

Present Medical Staff Category:

Attending _____ Active _____ Is the present appointment provisional: Yes _____ No _____

Requesting change in Medical Staff category: Yes _____ No _____

Expiration Date of current appointment: _____

1. **Office Location(s)**

   _____

   Medical Center Address (if any)   Mail Location   Office Telephone Number

   _____

   Other Office Address

   _____

   City   State   Zip Code   Office Telephone Number

2. **Home Address**

   _____

   Home Street Address

   _____

   City   State   Zip Code   Home Telephone Number

3. **Licensure/Registration**

   State Medical License Number _____

                                                    Expiration Date

   Other State Medical Licenses (Past Five Years or Present)

   _____

   State   License No.   Date Issued or Renewed

   _____

   State   License No.   Date Issued or Renewed

   _____

   State   License No.   Date Issued or Renewed

   _____

   DEA Registration Number _____

                          Date Issued   Expiration Date

   Please submit a copy of your state medical license and DEA registration.

4. **Certification**—Certification by Board, College or Equivalent. Does not refer to board-qualified or board-eligible status.

   _____

   Name   Date

   _____

   Name   Date

   _____

   If not certified, give current status:

   _____

Figure 6-2. (Continued)

5. **Continuing Education**—Please attach a list of the types of continuing education activities you have participated in during the past 24 months.

6. **Affiliations**

List current and previous Hospital affiliations in chronological order (present to past).

Name of Hospital	Category of Appointment	Inclusive Dates		
Street Address		City	State	Zip Code
Name of Hospital	Category of Appointment	Inclusive Dates		
Street Address		City	State	Zip Code
Name of Hospital	Category of Appointment	Inclusive Dates		
Street Address		City	State	Zip Code
Name of Hospital	Category of Appointment	Inclusive Dates		
Street Address		City	State	Zip Code

7. **Professional Liability Insurance**

List the malpractice insurance carrier providing liability coverage for your activity at the ABC Hospital. All members of the Medical Staff are required to have a minimum of 1 million per occurrence/1 million aggregate.

Carrier Name

Policy Number	Amount of Coverage	Effective Date	Expiration Date

A certificate of insurance must be submitted with this application unless you are covered by the ABC Hospital malpractice insurance program.

1. Have any malpractice claims been filed against you in the last five years?   Yes _____ No _____

2. Have any judgments been rendered against you or have any settlements been made on your behalf for professional liability cases, including law suits or claims, within the last five years?   Yes _____ No _____

3. Has your malpractice insurance coverage ever been terminated by action of an insurance company?   Yes _____ No _____

If YES, what company? _____

Date terminated

If the answer to any of the above questions is YES, please explain on a separate sheet. Statements regarding liability claims or settlements must include the following information: (1) Description of patient, (2) Brief history and chief complaints, (3) Procedures and treatments performed, along with hospital course, (4) Specific allegations of negligence, (5) Resolution of claim (pending, settled without payment, settled with payment and amount).

8. **Disciplinary Actions**

Have you ever entered a plea of guilty to, or has there ever been a judicial finding of guilty to a felony?   Yes _____ No _____

Have you ever entered a plea of guilty to, or has there ever been a judicial finding of guilty to a misdemeanor involving moral turpitude or to a misdemeanor committed in the course of practice?   Yes _____ No _____

Has any license or certificate of yours or your DEA number or its equivalent ever been denied, suspended, revoked, limited, or otherwise acted against?   Yes _____ No _____

Has your membership in any local, state, or national professional organization ever been revoked, suspended, reduced, not renewed, or challenged?   Yes _____ No _____

Have you ever been subject to disciplinary action in any professional organization?   Yes _____ No _____

Have you ever been allowed to resign your position rather than face any charge or investigation on the part of the Medical Staff?   Yes _____ No _____

Have you ever agreed to limit your clinical privileges in exchange for promise by an organization or entity not to initiate disciplinary action or to sanction you?   Yes _____ No _____

(Continued on next page)

Figure 6-2. (Continued)

Have your Medical Staff appointment and/or clinical privileges ever been denied, revoked, suspended, not renewed, or reduced other than automatic suspension of admitting privileges due to failure to complete medical records or due to poor quality medical records, at any health care facility?   Yes _____ No _____

Have you ever entered into a consent agreement, entered a plea of guilty, or found guilty of fraud or abuse involving payment of health care claims by any health care payer or been sanctioned by any third-party payer of health care claims or professional review organization, governmental entity, or agency?   Yes _____ No _____

If the answer to any of the above questions is YES, please explain on a separate sheet.

9. **Health Status**

Do you have a physical or mental condition which could affect your ability to exercise the clinical privileges requested or would require an accommodation in order for you to exercise the privileges requested safely and competently? To answer this question appropriately, please report any condition which is infectious, which affects motor skills, cognitive ability or judgment, or which may adversely affect your ability to care for patients or to interact appropriately with other caregivers.   Yes _____ No _____

Regardless of how this question is answered, the application will be processed in the usual manner. If you have answered this question affirmatively and are found to be professionally qualified for medical staff appointment and the clinical privileges requested, you will be given an opportunity to meet with the Physician's Health Task Force to determine what accommodations are necessary to allow you to practice safely.

To be Completed by the Department Clinical Chief

1. Is the applicant's performance satisfactory as reported to you by the following committees?

Surgical and Procedural Case Review	Yes _____	No _____	N/A _____
Medical Records	Yes _____	No _____	N/A _____
Infection Control	Yes _____	No _____	N/A _____
Utilization Review	Yes _____	No _____	N/A _____
Pharmacy and Therapeutics	Yes _____	No _____	N/A _____
Drug Use Evaluation	Yes _____	No _____	N/A _____
Transfusion Review	Yes _____	No _____	N/A _____
Patient Care Review	Yes _____	No _____	N/A _____

2. Has the applicant attended and participated in Medical Staff Meetings?   Yes _____ No _____ N/A _____

3. To your knowledge, has the physician been the subject of any complaints by:

Patients	Yes _____	No _____
Medical Staff Members	Yes _____	No _____
Nurses	Yes _____	No _____
Other Hospital Employees	Yes _____	No _____

4. To your knowledge, is there any physical or mental disability, including drugs or alcohol, which would prevent this physician from carrying out his responsibilities to his patients?   Yes _____ No _____

5. In your opinion, is there any privilege currently held by the applicant for which he does not possess the necessary skills and experience to perform appropriately?   Yes _____ No _____

If any answer to questions 3–5 is YES, please explain on a separate sheet.

_____   _____
Clinical Chief   Date

Applicant's Consent and Release

In applying for appointment, reappointment or clinical privileges as to the Medical Staff of ABC Hospital, I expressly accept these conditions during the processing and consideration of my application, regardless of whether or not I am granted reappointment or clinical privileges:

1. I release employees of ABC Hospital, the Hospital and its representatives, and any third parties, as defined in Article IV, Part A of the Medical Staff Bylaws, from any and all civil liability which might arise from any acts, communications, reports, recommendations or disclosures involving me concerning activities, including investigations, reviews, monitoring or evaluation, relating to my professional qualifications, credentials, clinical competence, clinical performance, character, mental or emotional stability, physical condition, ethics, behavior, or any other matter that might directly or indirectly have an effect on my competence, on patient care or on the orderly operation of the Hospital or any other hospital or health care facility, including otherwise privileged or confidential information. It is understood that the foregoing release from liability shall be limited to acts done or communications, reports, recommendations and disclosures made in good faith without malice.

Figure 6-2. (Continued)

2. Any act, communication, report, recommendation, or disclosure with respect to myself, made in good faith and at the request of an authorized representative of the Hospital or any other hospital or health care facility anywhere at anytime for the purposes set forth in (1) above, shall be privileged to the fullest extent permitted by law. Such privilege shall extend to employees of the Hospital, the Hospital and its representatives, and to any third parties, as these terms are defined in Article IV, Part A of the Medical Staff Bylaws, who either supply or are supplied information and to any of the foregoing authorized to receive, release or act upon same.

3. The Hospital and its representatives are specifically authorized to consult with the appointees to the medical staffs of other hospitals or health care facilities or the management of such hospitals or facilities with which I am or have been associated, and with others who may have information bearing on my professional qualifications, credentials, clinical competence, character, mental or emotional stability, physical condition, ethics, behavior or any other matter, as well as to inspect all records and documents that may be material to such questions. I grant immunity to any and all hospitals, health care facilities, third parties, individuals, institutions, organizations or their representatives who in good faith supply oral or written information, records or documents to the Hospital in response to any inquiry emanating from the Hospital or its authorized representatives.

4. I understand and agree that I have the burden of producing adequate information for proper evaluation of my professional qualifications, credentials, clinical competence, clinical performance, mental or emotional stability, physical condition, ethics, behavior or any other matter that might directly or indirectly have an effect on my competence, performance, patient care or orderly operation of the Hospital and for resolving any reasonable doubts about such qualifications.

5. I acknowledge my obligation to provide continuous care and supervision to all patients within the Hospital for whom I have responsibility.

6. I agree to abide by all such Bylaws, Rules and Regulations of the Medical Staff and policies of the Hospital as shall be in force during the time I am reappointed to the Medical Staff, and to any amendments thereto of which I have been duly notified. In addition, I agree to protect and keep confidential all personal or proprietary information or records that are stored manually or by electronic data processing.

7. I agree to accept committee assignments and such other reasonable duties and responsibilities as shall be assigned to me by the Board and the Medical Staff.

8. I have received and read a copy of such Medical Staff Bylaws and Rules and Regulations of the Medical Staff as are in force at the time of my reapplication and I agree to be bound by the terms thereof in all matters relating to consideration of my reapplication.

9. I have not requested privileges for any procedure for which I am not eligible or certified. Furthermore, I realize that certification by a Board does not necessarily qualify me to perform certain procedures. However, I believe that I am qualified to perform all procedures for which I have requested privileges.

10. I acknowledge that any misstatements or inaccuracies in or omissions from this application constitutes cause for denial of appointment or reappointment or cause for summary dismissal from the Medical Staff. All information submitted by me in the application is true to the best of my knowledge.

11. I am willing to appear for personal interviews in regard to my reapplication.

Signature

Enclosures Required

1. Photocopy of State Medical License
2. Photocopy of DEA Registration
3. Certificate of Professional Liability Insurance
4. List of Continuing Medical Education Activities
5. Delineation of Clinical Privileges signed by the Clinical Chief

---

Clinical Chief's Review:

I recommend the Applicants reappointment to the

_____ Attending Medical Staff _____ Active Medical Staff

Clinical Chief	Date
Credentials Committee Chairman	Date
Chief of Staff	Date
Board: Senior Vice President and Provost for Health Affairs	Date

Source: Adapted from a University of Cincinnati Hospital, Cincinnati, OH, form.

Objective Criteria

To maintain a sense of fairness to the physician applicant and all others on the medical staff, there should be as much consistency as possible in the credentialing process. Consistency is achieved by establishing a list of objective criteria that the hospital board can use to make a decision.

The information to be supplied is the same when objective criteria are applied to both new applications and reappointments. These include having a license to practice medicine, holding malpractice insurance to a limit specified by the hospital, and meeting certain educational requirements for specific privileges. Attendance at various continuing medical education (CME) programs also may be required.

In a new application, the credentials committee can only speculate on how the physician *might* perform if privileges were granted. Information on the physician must be obtained largely through references, sometimes from distant places. Rather than look for the impressions of references, it is far more accurate to examine objective criteria. Even with this approach, the hospital can never really know whether the applicant will be a suitable member of the medical staff until privileges are granted and utilized.

In an application for reappointment, a more thorough and accurate assessment can take place, because the hospital has already had direct and personal experience with the applicant, at least regarding the privileges the physician wishes to renew. Heavy reliance on references is no longer necessary unless the application for reappointment contains a request for privileges that were not included in the past. In that case, outside information is necessary in order to determine the applicant's capability for that aspect of the application. The Joint Commission on Accreditation of Healthcare Organizations (JCAHO) requires that (even for reappointment) the hospital solicit information from other hospitals where the physician has privileges. References also may be necessary to verify the standard of work that has been done outside the hospital, for example, in continuing education.

The credentialing process for reappointment should concentrate not only on the physician's capabilities, but also on his or her ability to be part of the hospital team and to work, regardless of his or her discipline, with hospital colleagues. A number of objective criteria can be established to indicate the level of participation and cooperation. The physician's performance can be compared to medical staff standards for the following:

- The percentage of committee and medical staff meetings a physician attended
- The number of times a physician failed to complete health records within the prescribed time limit
- The number of times a physician missed on-call duty or was late for on-call duty
- The number of CME credits or medical staff rounds that a physician accumulated during a particular time period
- The number of procedures the individual performed and their outcomes

All of these criteria can be evaluated exactly and do not require any subjective assessments. Nor does a committee or board have to exercise any discretion in determining whether the criteria have been met. Thus, objective criteria are very useful in helping to determine a physician's suitability for continuation of privileges at the hospital.

Subjective Criteria

The problem with reappointment is that the basis for making the judgment to reappoint can be highly subjective. Although there are basic minimum standards that all physicians should meet in carrying out certain procedures, there may be a wide divergence of opinion regarding other procedures.

The credentialing process involves human beings who are required to exercise judgment. How they exercise that judgment will differ from person to person. Some will be more aggressive in their approach, whereas others will be more passive and "let nature take its course." It is difficult to say that one body of opinion is superior to another. The profession may very well be divided on the issue. Whether one approach or the other is used also depends on the circumstances of specific cases.

Subjective criteria can be used in two ways, both of which can be helpful in assessing physician performance within the professional and social system. These criteria are the specific procedures performed by the physician and the physician's interpersonal relations within the hospital structure.

Specific Procedures

Information must be collected on specific procedures performed by that physician in the hospital, under what circumstances, in what manner, with what consultations, and using what support staff. This information can then be compared with that compiled for the "average" physician.

One problem with this method is that the physician under review may have patients who do not fall within the norm or circumstances may occur that place the patients at a higher risk than the average physician usually encounters. Thus, it may be unfair to compare the applicant's performance with the performance of the average physician. The fact that a physician may use techniques or approaches to patient care that are different from those used by other physicians does not mean that he or she is not performing competently in that hospital. Although there are certain basic standards to be met, to a large extent medicine is an art in which judgment and interpersonal relations play a very significant role.

Another problem with subjective evaluation is that of trying to determine what constitutes *average performance.* The average may be derived by comparing the performance of physicians across the country, across the state, in a region covering a number of states, or in a region within a single state. It also may be determined by comparing the care required for similar patients in similar-size hospitals. Regardless of the pool from which the average is taken, there is always the inherent danger that the standard determined for average performance will not provide an appropriate comparison on which to evaluate the work of the physician under review.

Interpersonal Relations

The second subjective criterion that can be used, and one that can cause difficulties if great care is not exercised, is that of interpersonal relations. Regardless of how competent a physician is, he or she must be able to work within the particular social structure of the hospital.

It is quite appropriate to inquire into whether the physician gets along with colleagues—particularly with nursing and support staff. Does he or she utilize nursing and support staff properly and treat them with courtesy and respect? Does he or she give instructions clearly and when needed? Does the physician respond to requests for advice or attendance?

All of these matters are extremely important in determining whether the physician should remain on staff. However, questions relating to interpersonal relations must be handled in context with all of the information received. A physician who gets along well with colleagues and hospital staff generally is a desirable asset to the medical staff and the hospital team. However, this aspect alone should not be used to reappoint a physician if the credentialing process shows that the physician is not clinically competent for the privileges requested or if he or she does not properly make use of the support services available.

On the other hand, a very competent and efficient physician who has difficulty getting along with others may be such a disruptive influence that his or her privileges should not be renewed. This is probably one of the more difficult issues in the reappointment and credentialing process, especially if some staff members relate well to the physician and others do not. Although difficult to apply, the criterion is a valid concern where there is no evidence of improved behavior.

Difficulty in applying subjective criteria does not mean that they should not be used in the credentialing process. Rather, subjective information must be considered *only* in the context within which it was collected and in order to give a complete picture of the applicant.

Proper Use of Quality Review Data in Reappointment Applications

Much information arising from continuing quality review can be useful in assessing the performance of a physician for the purpose of credentialing on a reappointment application. However, as with statistical data generally, great caution should be exercised in order to prevent developing a picture that is misleading or incorrect. To avoid such problems, a variety of reports and data should be evaluated as part of the quality process.

Drug Utilization Reports

Basic criteria should be established for the use of drugs in the hospital to determine whether such use is appropriate for various patients and follows guidelines that are developed nationally and within certain disciplines. It is important to track the use of drugs to ensure that patients are not overmedicated, that drugs are appropriate for the conditions for which they are prescribed, and that prescribed drugs are not contraindicated. This information should be collected with the help of the pharmacy and the medical records department and analyzed by the pharmacy and therapeutics committee of the medical staff.

Quality Improvement Data

The extent of the physician's involvement in the quality assessment (QA) program may be useful in determining a physician's involvement in the improvement of quality. However, great care must be taken in using these data, because it may be difficult to assess whether the physician under review had any real involvement in the success or failure of the quality improvement (QI) program. Matters may have improved in spite of the physician's involvement. However, at least having a physician involved in quality improvement that is working is better than having a physician who is not involved at all.

Other Statistics

Other statistics that should be examined in the credentialing process include morbidity and mortality statistics, surgical case review and other outcome data, infection control reports, blood utilization reviews, and diagnostic utilization reviews. With respect to utilization reviews, great care must be taken to obtain appropriate advice whether certain tests or treatments are overutilized or underutilized. The same can be said with respect to surgical case reviews when a question arises involving the propriety of specific procedures.

Statistics sometimes do not take into account variables such as severity of illness and complication factors. For example, medical charts may not contain accurate information regarding the indications for surgery and therefore the conclusions reached by a department QA/QI committee may be faulty.

To overcome these problems, special attention must be paid to that part of the credentialing process that involves peer review. Those who consider utilization and outcome data should be trained to put statistical data in context and to be able to use such data as one factor along with many others in assessing performance. It should not be assumed that medical experts on credentials or medical executive committees are trained in the use and interpretation of statistical data, regardless of how knowledgeable they are in their particular specialties and as clinicians.

The hospital also must gather statistical data in a way that is consistent, so that the review process is the same for all physicians and the basis on which recredentialing takes place is the same. Statistics relating to a particular procedure should be consistent over time so that the final data are reliable for the relevant time period. Additionally, reviewers should base their evaluations on the same number of cases at each review period, on the same type of cases, and on data collected in the same manner.

Before recommendations are made based on such data, the hospital should be certain that a sufficient number of cases or outcomes were used as the basis for a valid assessment and that the comparisons of patients and numbers and types of procedures properly match. There should be a proper control mechanism that takes into consideration the variables that might produce misleading results. If there are variables, there should be plausible explanations for them.

Occurrence Screening

As part of the credentialing process for a reappointment application, a review should take place of all unusual occurrences or incident reports involving the physician making the application. Analyzing the reports to determine whether there are weaknesses in his or her ability to perform various procedures, to work with other members of staff, or to appropriately use hospital facilities may provide information helpful in determining whether the clinician should be reappointed.

Occurrences that seem to illustrate a trend may be significant. Even these patterns, however, must be analyzed to determine the extent of the physician's involvement and whether an alteration or denial of all or certain privileges is appropriate.

Risk Management Reports

In addition to unusual occurrence and incident reports, any institution that has an operational risk management program will generate various risk management reports. These may include reports of matters such as medical orders that have been questioned or challenged by nurses or other staff members, interpersonal disputes, and complaints about general conduct.

Complaints about conduct may be directly related to either personal conduct or the performance of medical procedures. Personal conduct may be related to the way the physician has treated patients and/or family or other staff members, tardiness in keeping appointments, or failure to follow hospital procedures.

Risk management reports may have been developed using incident reports or from a number of other sources, including reports from nursing staff, minutes of medical staff committees, or letters or calls of complaint from patients or families. They also may have come from the office of the patient representative, or from some outside body such as an accrediting organization or a government agency.

In addition to incident reports and complaints, reports of potential claims against the applicant as well as actual lawsuits should be included in the risk management report. The report should note what the claim or suit was about, whether it indicated a clinical issue that should be considered in reappointment, and how the matter was resolved.

Additionally, any interim assessments that have been done on the physician during the term of the appointment and any conclusions that were reached at that time should be reported. The report on interim assessments should include any information on what suggestions were made, if any, to the physician and what action was taken as a result.

A system must be established to bring all of these documents together so that the data form the basis of the credentialing process. As with all other reports, care must be taken to ensure the veracity of the information and to determine whether the incidents are of such significance that the only means of correction is to restrict or deny privileges.

Because many of the reports may be based on highly subjective information, the information given should be regarded as being useful as a *possible* indicator of physician ability to hold privileges and not as the determining factor by itself. With all the information taken together, the medical staff committees and the board will be able to create a profile of the physician in order to appropriately assess the reappointment application. (See figure 6-3 for a sample performance evaluation form.)

Applicant's Right to Challenge Quality Review Data

As detailed in chapter 2, the concept of fairness and all legal requirements of due process must be observed during the credentialing process. To this end, when questions are raised regarding an applicant, he or she must be given the opportunity to provide additional information that will help the credentials committee and the medical executive committee make a recommendation for reappointment to the medical staff. The physician should be encouraged to provide further information on such matters as preintervention indicators for treatment, postintervention findings, and specific patient information that may explain or account for variations. Much of this information may be in the physician's own records and not necessarily in the patient's hospital medical record.

The physician also must have an opportunity to challenge the validity of the data and the manner in which they were collected. Additionally, he or she must be given the opportunity to bring in outside experts to support these challenges and any challenges to conclusions the hospital may have made on the basis of the information.

The purpose of the credentialing process is not to bring in or keep out physicians; rather, its purpose is to ensure that high-quality medical care is provided to the hospital's patients. Decisions on an application for reappointment must be made with this in mind. If this goal can be achieved without altering privileges, that attempt should at least be considered.

Data Bank and Other Inquiries

As discussed in chapter 5, any initial application for privileges must include an inquiry to the National Practitioner Data Bank and could include an inquiry to the Federation of State Boards of Medical Licensure to determine whether there is any matter on record that would influence the decision to grant privileges. It is just as important to make a further inquiry in an application for reappointment. In this way, information that has been put in the file since the previous granting of privileges can become apparent. It also will provide notice if an occurrence has taken place in another hospital in which the physician holds privileges. This information may not otherwise be known to the hospital where the reappointment is sought. As with other information, assumptions

Figure 6-3. Sample Clinical Care and Performance Evaluation Form

(Note: This document is to be completed by the department chairperson when application is made for reappointment for staff privileges by a member of the department.)

Applicant's Name _____   Date _____

Current Privileges: _____   Requested Privileges Delineation _____

Please supply the following information regarding the applicant's professional performance since the last application for appointment to the medical staff. An answer marked no should be explained in greater detail on a separate sheet of paper.

	Yes	No	N/A
The applicant has met the minimum number of procedures required to maintain privileges delineation.	___	___	___
The applicant's outcomes have been acceptable.	___	___	___
The applicant has participated in the required number of continuing medical education programs.	___	___	___
The applicant has participated in clinically oriented departmental staff meetings/rounds.	___	___	___
The applicant has provided required on-call coverage.	___	___	___
The applicant has responded to requests to return to the hospital to see patients.	___	___	___
The applicant has provided timely and accurate completion of health records.	___	___	___
The applicant has demonstrated an acceptable level of professional judgment.	___	___	___
The applicant has demonstrated an acceptable level of technical skill.	___	___	___
The applicant has demonstrated an acceptable level of patient management.	___	___	___
The applicant has demonstrated an acceptable degree of communication skills with patients and their families.	___	___	___
The applicant has demonstrated an acceptable degree of communication skills with other health professionals.	___	___	___
The applicant has adhered to hospital bylaws, policies, and procedures.	___	___	___

Please indicate if the applicant has ever performed procedures or ordered tests that on peer review were deemed inappropriate or unacceptable.

_____

_____

_____

_____

Please indicate if the applicant has ever been the subject of questioned orders from other physicians or health professionals that on peer review were deemed appropriately challenged. _____

_____

_____

The applicant has requested the following changes in delineated privileges. _____

_____

_____

_____

As department chairperson, do you agree that the applicant has the requisite skill, training, experience, and demonstrated clinical competency for the requested delineated privileges? _____

Please explain your response, including any qualifications or conditions you recommend should be placed on the applicant's privileges.

_____

_____

_____

_____

Name of Department Chairperson _____   Date _____

Please attach relevant outcome data to support answers provided on this form.

should not be made that the information is correct or that it reflects on the physician's competency. In addition, as with other evidence to be considered, complete disclosure must be given to the physician, who should be given the opportunity to explain any information received from either body.

Handling Rejection of Reappointment Applications or Curtailment of Privileges

The decision to reject an application for the renewal of privileges or to curtail or modify a physician's privileges must be reached in the same way that it is with a new application. (See chapter 5.) During the credentialing process, hospital bylaws and state legislation and regulations must be followed scrupulously. Rules of due process and fairness must be established, circulated, and understood by board members, advisory and review committee members, and the medical staff.

A code of procedure should be drafted so that everyone involved can follow and understand the procedure. Additionally, the procedure cannot treat physicians unfairly on the basis of incorrect or misleading information or on information or opinion that is not available to the physician and open to his or her comment, analysis, and examination.

Any physician whose privileges are revoked or curtailed has the right to mount a challenge consistent with state law and the health facility's bylaws. In many instances a physician's rights include the following:

- Have the opportunity to present additional information
- Criticize the information already presented
- Be heard by an unbiased body
- Understand the basis on which decisions are made

(See chapter 2 for a full discussion of the legal rights of the physician.)

It is important to note that a decision may be made on the basis that the physician is no longer competent to perform the privileges that were previously exercised or that the hospital can no longer support the privileges being sought. It also should be noted that in the case of the physician who is no longer competent, this may not be due to a decrease in the his or her competency. Rather, it may be that standards have changed and the physician's skills have not kept pace with the changing standards.

Consideration for an appeal, or at least a second review, for those applications that have been rejected or modified should be given. This procedure should be carried out in accordance to with the medical staff bylaws.

Criteria also should be established when a hospital that at one time could support certain procedures can no longer do so. This also gives physicians an opportunity to alter their practices.

Invariably, a finding that a physician or surgeon is no longer competent to hold certain privileges has developed during the time the physician has held privileges at the hospital. Therefore, credentialing should not be a process that takes place only when the physician applies for a reappointment to the medical staff. Continuing or at least periodic assessments must be made so that developing problems can be brought to the physician's attention and corrected. Frequently, the problem is that the physician is applying for privileges to perform procedures that he or she seldom performs in actual practice and simply cannot demonstrate current clinical competence. Notifying the physician will allow him or her to either meet the criteria or alter the next application for reappointment accordingly, thus reducing the risk of confrontation and potential litigation over a rejection or curtailment.

Conclusion

In the past, a physician's reappointment to the medical staff was virtually automatic. However, in recent years, reappointment privileges have been granted for a fixed period, at the end of which the physician must reapply. The credentialing process for reappointment involves basically the same steps as required in the process for initial appointment and must likewise observe due process considerations required by law and specified in the hospital's bylaws in the event that reappointment privileges are either rejected or curtailed.

The process involves evaluation of both objective and subjective criteria that can indicate the physician's practice capabilities, as well as his or her ability to work with colleagues and medical staff and to work within the institution's rules. Particularly in the reappointment process, the credentials committee can collect information on the physician from quality review data, including drug utilization reports, quality improvement data, risk management reports, and so on. In addition, the committee seeks out information from the National Practitioners Data Bank.

7 | Suspension, Restriction, and Revocation of Privileges

Introduction

No physician has the legal right to demand hospital privileges regardless of whether the hospital is private or public.[1] However, this does not mean that the hospital's board of trustees or administration may suspend, restrict or revoke privileges at will. Even if a privileges action is justified, certain legal requirements must be met. These legal requirements may be found in common law (that is, the law as developed by the courts over the years), state and federal legislation or regulation, or hospital bylaws. The legal authority serves a number of purposes. First, it authorizes whatever action is to be taken against the physician's privileges. Second, it establishes the conditions on which the action is taken. And third, it sets up a procedure by which the action is taken and gives authority to various individuals or bodies within the institution to take the action.

Failure to follow this legal framework may result in the action taken against the physician's privileges being declared invalid by a court. In this case, the court's decision may not only reestablish the physician's privileges, but award the physician monetary compensation for the facility's wrongful action.

Over the past few years, the practice has been for physicians and hospitals to develop written directions on how to take disciplinary actions, rather than leaving them to be decided on a case-by-case basis and at the hospital's discretion. In other words, physicians are made aware of the rules of potential suspension, restriction, and revocation before any privileges arrangement is entered into.

This chapter discusses the various requirements that must be considered in following a legal and appropriate procedure for handling privileges actions. It also describes the importance of keeping accurate documentation and maintaining hospital–physician communication in order to avoid a privileges action.

Bylaw Requirements

One method of establishing the legal basis for taking an action against a physician's privileges has been to include it in the hospital's or medical staff's bylaws. Its inclusion in the bylaws may be done either at the initiative of the hospital or pursuant to accreditation, or it may be required by state legislation. However, the fact that state legislation mandates certain requirements to be included in the bylaws with respect to any action affecting privileges does not mean that the hospital cannot add additional requirements.

For example, the Public Health Act of Massachusetts[2] requires that the bylaws of every licensed hospital and those of all medical staffs shall contain provisions for reporting conduct by a health care provider that indicates incompetence in his or her specialty or that might be inconsistent with or harmful to good patient care or safety. However, the legislation does not specify what conduct is to be reported. The question to be addressed by the hospital and its legal counsel in drafting bylaws is whether the bylaws should be more specific.

Specificity versus Generality

The advantage to making the bylaws specific is that the administration can take a disciplinary action without its decision to do so appearing to be discretionary. The disadvantage is that often a physician's conduct that should result in action against privileges may not, because the bylaws do not specifically require that action to be taken. One way to overcome this problem is to incorporate specificity and, at the same time, to permit a certain degree of open-endedness. For example, the bylaws may require that action be taken against a physician in a number of specific cases and, in addition, in such other circumstances as determined by the board from time to time.

Although this approach would give the hospital a degree of flexibility, its vagueness creates difficulties of interpretation. Additionally, it moves away from the general principles of fairness that permit all parties involved in the privileges process to know what it is they have to face and by what rules they are governed.

In other instances, state legislation may be so strict that it leaves little room for divergence. Therefore, in drafting bylaws, close attention must be paid to the legislation to determine what legal requirements the hospital must, may, and must not include in its bylaws.

In some states, legislation may mandate a requirement but not require the hospital to include it in its bylaws. For example, the Massachusetts legislation[3] referenced earlier in this chapter also requires that when a medical peer review committee of a licensed hospital determines that a health care provider's privileges should be suspended in the best interests of patient care, the committee shall immediately forward its recommendation to the executive committee of the medical staff and the board of trustees for action. However, the legislation does not state that this requirement *must* be included in the bylaws, even though it is binding on the institution and gives the physician certain rights.

If a hospital were to include this requirement in its bylaws, the requirement would be neither strengthened nor weakened; it would simply be duplicated. The danger in duplicating the requirement is that its inclusion in a different context could be interpreted to mean that it has a different meaning. The requirements may be seen as applicable only in certain circumstances under bylaws, but in others under legislation. This can only add to confusion and could become a possible source of conflict. A further danger is that if the legislation were to change, the provision in the bylaws would then be in conflict with the legislation if the institution failed to make the necessary amendment. This is just one of the many reasons why the hospital's legal counsel should constantly monitor all appropriate state and federal legislation, common-law provisions, and accreditation provisions to ensure that the institution's bylaws are in conformity.

Combination of Bylaws and Rules/Regulations

Another approach to dealing with the disadvantage of specificity is to distinguish between the bylaws and any rules or regulations made pursuant to the bylaws. The advantage to this approach is that the bylaws usually are more complicated to change procedurally than are rules and regulations. The board is invariably involved in bylaw changes, but, generally, rules can often be changed by administration. Changes in bylaws may also require certain voting criteria, such as a certain percentage majority. The feasibility of this approach depends in large part on what is required by the institution and the state to pass or amend the hospital's bylaws.

One drawback to having requirements in different places is that administrators and physicians must then consult more than one document in order to govern themselves in these matters. Additionally, the two documents must be read as if they were in fact one, which many readers find difficult to do. Another drawback is that either the rule or regulation, or the application of the rule, may conflict with the bylaw. As "subsidiary" legislation, the rule or regulation would obviously be subject to any provision in the bylaw. However, this too may create a basis for controversy and conflict that might otherwise be avoided. For example, the physician's right to have access to hospital documents and the procedure of obtaining them may be in two different sources. Unless the two sources are read together, the reader may only get half the picture and may be mislead into thinking that one procedure applies to all criteria.

Additionally, changes made in one document can affect the wording of another. Consequently, in addition to being involved in the drafting of bylaws or any other internal document with respect to hospital actions that could affect a physician's privileges, legal counsel should educate and advise the board and medical staff on the use of such documents.

Use of Statistical Data and Interdisciplinary Reports

The use of statistical data to provide continuing assessment of medical staff performance can be extremely helpful but also very dangerous. It is dangerous when such data are used as the basis for suspending, restricting, or revoking privileges, because use of the information creates a risk of unfairness to the physician involved if no explanation is made to the physician of how the data are applied. As a result, the physician whose privileges have been affected could base a lawsuit on the improper use of these data.

The major problem with using quality review data is that they frequently are not an appropriate measure for determining the quality of care given by a particular physician, nor are they always an accurate way of measuring the physician's competence. For example, data collected on surgical patients who had to be returned to the operating room (OR) do not, by themselves, reflect the quality of care generally in the OR or the competence of the surgeon or the anesthesiologist. The fact that a particular surgeon has a higher rate of return than other surgeons does not necessarily mean that he or she operates at a lower level of competence. Rather, it may mean that this surgeon takes on cases that have greater inherent risks, that the type of surgery may be different, or that preoperatively the patients are in a more serious condition. In fact, the surgeon may be more competent than others and better able to take on higher-risk patients who naturally are more likely to be returned to the OR.

As credentialing becomes more multidisciplinary, professionals other than physicians may be asked their opinion on a particular physician's performance, which may have a direct bearing on whether he or she will be reappointed or restricted. For example, it is quite proper to ask nurses whether a particular physician relates well to the nursing staff, gives medical orders clearly, or makes proper use of nursing services. These questions are all appropriate for nurses and their answers may be very useful in determining whether the physician's current privileges should be maintained. The nurses' answers may be affected by personal relationships with the physician and thus may be highly subjective. Therefore, information of this sort should not be relied on to be the sole determinant in the assessment of privileges.

Procedural Considerations

Frequently, suspending, restricting, or revoking a physician's privileges has little to do with the merits of the case. Often, the problem lies in whether the correct procedure has been followed in determining the action to be taken against the physician.

Following the Rules

The first major error that is often made, and the one that can be most easily avoided, is that the institution did not heed the various written enactments governing the credentialing process. This includes legislation, bylaws and regulations, and any other requirements that bind the hospital, such as a contract between the institution and an accrediting body, a contract between the institution and a medical group or association authorized to enter into the contract with the hospital on behalf of its members or those of its members who have privileges.

Reviewing the Procedure

The due process requirements also affect the manner in which decisions are made and can affect the merits of these decisions as well. Due process requirements can affect not only the actual procedure used, but also the validity of the written rules under bylaws. Because it is not always clear whether a procedure, written or otherwise, offends due process, it is important that legal counsel be asked to review the procedure. In addition, legal counsel should be asked to educate the various committees and the board as well as their administrative officers on the correct procedure.

Putting It in Writing

The process for taking privileges actions should be set in writing so that can be easily read and followed by medical staff and various committees and administrative officials. The process must conform to legal requirements mentioned previously.

Avoiding Disputes, If Possible

From a risk management point of view, a procedural dispute can be expensive and disruptive and can be avoided or at least minimized. Therefore, the approach frequently taken is that if there is any doubt whether a physician has a particular procedural right, it is often preferable that the hospital accede to that right as long as inordinate health care resources are not required to grant the right. In the same fashion, the hospital should resist attempts made by the physician's attorney to turn a hearing into a trial-type procedure with all the trappings of procedural distractions. For example, if an adjournment during a hearing on a privileges action is requested on questionable grounds, or if a witness is called whose qualifications are in some doubt, it frequently is better to allow the request rather than divert attention to a dispute over what is clearly not the central issue. At some point, however, tactics that are obviously inappropriate must be controlled.

Furthermore, institutions are unlikely to enhance their reputation if they discipline a physician on a point that the lay public refers to as "a technicality." Needless to say, although it is important to consider all the factors, it is equally important to keep in mind that the hospital's main purpose is to maintain a medical staff of competent physicians who work well with their colleagues and support staff and who meet the hospital's mission of providing a reasonable standard of care to its patients. In the heat of a dispute, that purpose frequently is sidetracked by the desire to win points of law and procedure.

Observing Due Process

The key principle in any procedure can be summed up in the words *no surprises.* Everyone should know exactly what the issues are and what information is to be presented. This means that any complaint brought against a physician must be made known in adequate detail so that the physician can consult legal counsel, collect the necessary information, obtain professional advice, and prepare a defense. (See chapter 2.) Without being advised of the details of the complaint, the physician has legitimate grounds for complaining that the proceedings are invalid.

It is important that members of the decision making body be aware of these basic procedural rights of the physician whose privileges may be in jeopardy in order to avoid any allegations of impropriety. In practice, this means accepting the principle that no information or allegations must come before the body that have not been previously presented in the presence of the physician.

This principle applies not only when the decision is being made, but also when the various committee or board members are asking questions. No question should be prefaced or based on anything that any member has heard or seen other than on information that has been presented before that body in the physician's presence. The proceedings should be followed so as not to provoke even a suspicion of bias, however remote that suspicion may be.

Determining the Procedure of the Hearing Committee

Generally, it is most effective for the hearing body to have established procedure before the hearing begins and then to make its decision only on the basis of what committee members hear and see in the presence of the physician and his or her counsel. To ensure that the procedure is carried out, the hearing body may wish to engage independent counsel, paid for by the institution, who may wish to draft a statement that describes the instructions on the procedure and how the decision will be reached. This statement can then be read by the person presiding. Such a statement should be given to the physician's lawyer well in advance of the hearing, so that he or she will be able to present the doctor's case as fairly and completely as possible without any suggestion that the case was prejudiced by procedural surprises or unfamiliarity. (Note: The institution's lawyer should not be advising the hearing body because that individual will also be representing the institution against the physician. It would be a conflict of interest to serve in both roles and unfair to the physician.)

When issues arise requiring a procedural ruling, great care should be taken not to create the basis for a legal challenge on procedural matters. It is advisable to be as flexible as possible with respect to requests by the physician or his or her counsel, as long as the requests are reasonable and would not jeopardize the ability of the board or committee to fully assess the information available and make an informed and fair decision.

Attempts to reach an agreement with the physician or his or her counsel also may be useful. Using either of these approaches will make it much more difficult for the physician to challenge a decision on procedural grounds at a later date. In either case, careful documentation must be kept to provide evidence that procedural fairness and correctness were in fact followed. Mediation of a dispute, often by bringing in a third-party mediator, may assist in removing any personal antagonisms. A voluntary reduction of privileges may be agreeable to a physician who faces the termination of all privileges.

Documentation Requirements

In any case affecting a physician's privileges, a legal challenge to disciplinary action depends to a great extent on whether the physician can prove that the action was arbitrary or capricious or based on some unlawful motive. Such proof can be by either the testimony of witnesses or written documentation.

Testimony of Witnesses

At the hearing, evidence presented by witnesses based on recall can always be challenged. The fact is that a witness's memory is likely to change over time. People either forget the facts or intentionally (or unintentionally) change them in their attempt to recall the circumstances. Since the original event or series of events that prompted the disciplinary action against the physician, various other influences may have affected the witnesses' recollection. For example, they may have repeated their recollection of the events to various administrative officials, colleagues, and lawyers so often that the truth has become cloudy, if not completely altered. In addition, even if witnesses can accurately recall the events in question, the suspicion always lingers that accurate recall is unlikely.

Written Documentation

The alternate method of proof is written documentation that was recorded accurately at the time the events occurred. To be effective, the documentation must provide evidence that supports the hospital against any allegations brought by an aggrieved physician.

For example, the physician may claim that the process by which his or her privileges were altered did not conform to the process required by appropriate legislation, regulations, or hospital bylaws. To ensure that such a claim is unsubstantiated, all the various requirements should be carefully reviewed and incorporated into a checklist. This checklist would then be documented with specific references as to how it is to be applied to the particular case. For example, these references would indicate that certain documentation needs to be collected and filed and that certain actions must be taken on or before a specified date. The person responsible for handling the case will then know what to collect, when to collect it, and where to file it.

In addition to written requirements, other requirements may need to be fulfilled under the general principles of due process of law, and, in consultation with legal counsel, should be added to the checklist. These would include:

- Statistical data and their supporting documentation
- Incident reports and analyses of those reports
- Evidence being used to support a case for the discipline of the physician and/or the suspension, restriction, or revocation of his or her privileges
- Notices to the physician of problems and reports of minutes of meetings in which those problems were discussed
- Records of any hearings or committee meetings
- Statements to the effect that the documents are accurate copies of the originals and that they have not been altered

Steps to Avoid a Privileges Action

Nothing can be more disruptive to a hospital or a community than a medical staff privileges dispute. It pits colleagues against each other and frequently places nurses and other health care staff in the position of appearing to be disloyal to those with whom they work. In small communities, board members and physicians who maintain close social and community ties may become embroiled in bitter conflict. Patients also may be brought into conflict with various support committees organized to defend a popular physician against other physicians. Frequently, the dispute is discussed in the local media, as well as in social, recreational, and religious circles. The effects from such events can last for years and can have a negative impact on all concerned, as well as on the institution's ability to attract community support and cooperation. If a lawsuit is filed, the matter becomes public and the damage to the hospital's reputation and goodwill is difficult to control.

Thus, every effort should be made to avoid situations in which privileges actions are necessary. Unfortunately, the reality is that difficulties frequently are not dealt with before a procedure of formal hearings goes into place. By that point, the positions of both parties have become formalized, and on the basis of legal advice, little flexibility is possible because of the fear of placing legal rights in jeopardy.

One way to try to ensure that the two parties do not reach a point of no return is to open the lines of communication between the hospital and its medical staff. Communication should begin as soon as a physician applies for staff privileges and should continue throughout the extension of those privileges.

Communication at the Time of Application for Privileges

Medical staff problems invariably arise as a result of a continuing pattern of behavior over a period of time, rather than a single occurrence. This behavior often has not been corrected because the physician and the institution have never effectively dealt with it. Thus, it is important that every applicant to the medical staff receive in writing a clear statement, usually in the medical staff bylaws, explaining that the granting of staff privileges gives the physician permission (not a right) to enter its premises and use its facilities, equipment and supplies, and staff for the purpose of treating that physician's private patients. However, this permission is granted with certain limits and conditions.

The physician must abide by the limits of the privileges that have been granted and undertake certain obligations to the institution. Although these vary from hospital to hospital, generally they include providing advice through membership on various committees and participating in an on-call service or providing emergency care at various times.

In addition, the physician must meet certain standards of care as set by the hospital from time to time; carry on practice according to certain professional and ethical standards; and abide by the various procedures, rules, regulations, policies, and bylaws of the hospital. As a member of the staff, the physician is subject to various disciplinary procedures and actions if it is found that the standards and conditions on which privileges have been granted have not been met. Any action the institution pursues that may result in the suspension, restriction, or revocation of privileges will only be taken in accordance with its procedures, rules, regulations, policies and bylaws, and, of course, any other requirements imposed by law.

Physicians do not always understand that they have various obligations as well as rights, or they do not understand what those obligations are. Many institutions and their advisory committees, particularly the board and medical staff, also do not fully appreciate the details of the physician–hospital relationship. This lack of understanding may be traced to a time less than a generation ago when the physician–hospital relationship was far more casual and less structured.

Thus, it is recommended that the application for privileges contain a written explanation of the details of the proposed relationship, the obligations of both parties in that relationship, and the consequences of not fulfilling those obligations. Good communication therefore, must begin *before* the physician even becomes part of the staff. Once medical staff privileges have been granted, further communication should take place clarifying the hospital's unique relationship with that particular physician.

Ongoing Communication through Mediation

Communication also is important when one party or the other feels that the obligations under the medical staff relationship are not being met. For the physician merely to mention his or her concern to a colleague, for example, and then complain that nothing was done cannot be considered communication. This is particularly true if the person to whom the concern was mentioned has no authority to act on the matter. Thus, it is important that the hospital monitor the medical staff by designating an individual who can maintain close and regular contact with each physician.

Mediating Complaints and Allegations

Communication between a hospital-designated contact and the physician may be relatively informal in order to resolve a complaint that may have been simply a misunderstanding and not really a problem at all. Even so, a record should be made of the complaint, the discussion that ensued, and the conclusion of the discussion.

However, if informal communication proves to be ineffective, or if it involves a matter in which informal discussion is not appropriate, such as immediate suspension, formal communication should take place. Formal communication should follow a standard practice such as a written notification of the allegations. Any reports or data that might affect that physician's privileges should be discussed with the physician as quickly as possible, and a specific time frame should be established during which action for change is required. Failure to maintain close contact with the physician and to assist in taking remedial action can lead to a privileges dispute that may not be necessary.

Another reason that communication must be effective is to ensure that the action taken by the physician is the action requested and an appropriate response to the allegations being made. If the language and methods used by the hospital in the communication process are not effective, it is difficult to criticize the physician for not complying. It is even more difficult for the hospital to impose disciplinary action based on an allegation that the physician has either misunderstood or has not been made aware of.

Mediating Corrective Education

If, through discussion and consultation, it is found that the physician is not meeting appropriate standards, a voluntary responsive plan should be put into place. This may require further education in some areas. If this is the case, a deadline should be established and monitored to ensure that the required education is satisfactorily completed. Consultation may be necessary to ensure that the recommended education will in fact be appropriate to the problem areas in the physician's practice. However, it would be improper to require continuing education to be taken that is not available to the physician because of either the program's location or its schedule.

Ideally, with good communication the physician will voluntarily enter a program to meet the standards required. In the meantime, the hospital should not allow the current situation in which practice is substandard to continue. The physician should be asked to voluntarily limit his or her use of privileges so as not to infringe the standards. If a voluntary restriction takes place, it is important that it be documented and that the appropriate hospital officials be notified.

If further education is not appropriate or available to correct the situation, a voluntary restriction may become permanent. This would necessitate a formal letter from the physician seeking a change. This request should be reviewed by the appropriate medical staff and administrative committee to ensure that the change in privileges will have the desired result. Voluntary relinquishment of privileges related to the physician's quality of care must also be reported to the National Practitioner Data Bank.

No formal hearings would be required and no finding of fault or condemnation would go on the physician's record. From the hospital's point of view, this action removes the possibility of a very disruptive event and, it is hoped, the potential for patient injury resulting from the failure to meet standards. For the physician, the practice can continue in those areas in which appropriate standards can reasonably be met.

It also may be possible to settle such a dispute by bringing in an outside third party as a mediator. However, the question that arises is whether the mediator will simply try to bring the parties together or make a decision. If a decision is made, the question is whether it should be binding on both parties. This could be difficult for a hospital that might then be left with a physician whom it does not want and who may be below a standard the hospital feels is acceptable.

Steps to Take in the Event of a Privileges Action

In every action taken against a physician that might affect the continuation of medical staff privileges, the physician's defense might take the form of counterallegations. The physician might first assert that the allegations are not true. Second, the physician might challenge the procedure followed in the suspension, restriction, or revocation of the privileges. And third, the physician could say that the grounds on which the allegations are made are not proper for the action being proposed or for actions that have already been taken.

To forestall these defenses and, on a more positive note, to prevent such events from occurring, the institution would be well advised to document its actions in order to support their propriety. As mentioned in the earlier section on written documentation, a file should be established that contains documentation that supports the grounds on which the hospital proposes action, copies of the appropriate procedure along with documentary evidence that this procedure has been followed, and documentation that demonstrates the basis on which the proposed action would be appropriate assuming that the facts for the action were proved to be correct. The procedure may be contained in bylaws, policies, or other documentation. No action should be taken unless it is supported by the information found in the documentation.

A number of actions should be taken when a lawsuit is initiated as a result of privileges being altered by the hospital. At the first hint of action, all records of any proceedings against the physician, his or her personnel, and all records on which any opinion was based regarding the privileges should be collected and placed in safekeeping. No alterations must be made to the records and no records should be removed by anyone other than legal counsel, except in his or her presence.

All documents, bylaws and rules, regulations, or policies respecting privileges for the time period in question should be collected and separated, along with any legislation or regulations and accreditation or other legal documents that may affect privileges. A complete review of the proceedings should take place in light of all these documents to determine whether any errors may have been made in procedure. Additionally, every individual who was involved in the action resulting in an alteration of privileges should be noted and interviewed by the risk manager or legal counsel to determine that the procedure and the substance of the decision were appropriate.

A decision should be made as quickly as possible to determine whether any errors of law or fact have been made and whether the hospital has grounds for a defense to the physician's counteraction. Once this decision has been made, the board of trustees should weigh its legal position against the political and public relations realities of a lawsuit, even one that could be successfully defended by the institution. The ultimate cost of winning the suit may be greater than the cost of making a compromise, as long as the quality of patient care in the institution is not adversely affected.

Conclusion

State legislation, rules and regulations imposed by various accrediting bodies, and hospital bylaws combine to provide a legal framework for hospitals taking steps to suspend, restrict, or revoke a physician's privileges. A hospital's failure to follow this framework could result in its actions being challenged by the physician and found invalid in a court of law. Thus, hospitals should make every attempt to observe due process requirements in order, first, to avoid taking a privileges action and, second, if action is taken, to provide a defense in the event the physician takes a counteraction.

The principal way to ensure that procedural requirements are met is to have the hospital's legal counsel participate in the drafting of the bylaws to ensure their compliance with legislation. In addition, legal counsel should work with the hospital's board and medical staff to ensure that they are aware of and understand the requirements. Key to monitoring procedural compliance is the ongoing collection and maintenance of written documentation.

However, hospitals would be wise to attempt to avoid taking actions against physicians by opening the lines of communication with their medical staff. This would begin by clarifying the physician–hospital relationship in writing at the time the physician applies for privileges. It would then continue throughout the physician's appointment through the designation of a contact person to work with each physician on perceived problems and their possible resolution. In many cases, open communication and ongoing cooperation can prevent disciplinary actions from being taken that ultimately would be harmful to both the hospital and the physician.

References

1. Southwick, A. F. *The Law of Hospital and Health Care Administration.* 2nd ed. Ann Arbor, MI: Health Administration Press, 1988, c. 14; *Hayman v. Galvesten,* 273 U.S. 414, 416–17 (1927). *See also,* Dellinger, A. M. *Health Care Facilities Law.* Boston: Little Brown, 1991, c. 1.

2. Mass. Genl. Laws, c.111, s.203.

3. Mass. Genl. Laws.

8 | Economic Credentialing and Emerging Issues and Trends

Introduction

The more care that physicians provide to a hospitalized patient, the more money they make; the more care that hospitals provide, the less money they make. Under the current reimbursement system for health care, physicians charge a fee for each service, test, or procedure they perform. Hospitals, on the other hand, are paid a fixed amount (the diagnosis-related group [DRG] amount) by Medicare and Medicaid based on the patient's diagnosis, regardless of the number of tests and procedures ordered. Depending on what their contracts with insurance companies provide, hospitals also may be reimbursed a fixed amount for patients insured by third-party payers. A struggle develops between the hospital and its physicians because hospitals have little influence over physician practice patterns despite the fact that practice patterns determine the resources that go into the care of patients and those resources are a large part of the hospital's costs. To preserve their revenues, hospitals are finding ways either to encourage physicians to be more conscious of the cost of care or to incorporate cost information into the credentialing process.

This chapter discusses the concept of economic credentialing, including the physician response to the concept, the legal basis for it, the traditional forms of the concept, and the future of economic credentialing. In addition, this chapter examines two emerging issues that are beginning to have an impact on medical staff privileges.

Economic Credentialing

Using information systems technology, hospitals have the ability to measure the cost of tests and procedures and the length of the patient's hospital stay, attribute the data to the patient's physician, and then compare those data against whatever benchmark the hospital selects. For example, a hospital can compare the way an orthopedist treats an 85-year-old woman who undergoes a hip replacement against a composite profile of all orthopedists in the same metropolitan area who treat similar cases to see whether the patient's length of stay and the costs incurred compare favorably. Through their training and practice, individual physicians develop their own standard ways of treating specific diseases, but do not customarily share their treatment protocols with others in the same specialty to see whether they might adopt more cost-efficient protocols. If physicians were accustomed to prescribing treatment with costs in mind, the data hospitals gather would be welcomed instead of feared. Clinical pathways and practice parameters may lead the charge to this new way of using such information.

One way that hospitals could use the data they are able to gather is to incorporate economics into the credentialing process as another measure of physician performance in deciding whether a physician should be a member of the medical staff, what category of membership the physician should be approved for, and what privileges the physician should be granted. Economic credentialing is one weapon in the same arsenal hospital administrators have recently acquired to control physician practice patterns. Other weapons include the development of practice parameters and outcomes research by groups such as the Agency for Health Care Policy and Research and the Uniform Clinical Data Set, computerized treatment algorithms developed by the Health Care Financing Administration for peer review organizations' Fourth Scope of Work. The goal of all these systems is to bring physician practice into conformance with protocols that are more efficient than individual physicians develop without the benefit of research and consultation with peers.

Instead of making patient care decisions using resources available with little cognizance of their cost, physicians will be encouraged, or even coerced, to follow standardized treatment protocols developed by physician groups inside or outside the hospital using data describing outcomes, costs, and risks and benefits. The physician groups within the hospital that recognize the value of the data are beginning to work with other health care professionals in the hospital to develop critical pathways for caring for particular diseases. A *critical pathway* is a plan for treating a particular condition that describes what tests and treatments the patient will receive and the timing of these procedures. Quality, cost, efficiency, and reduced length of stay are all factored into the protocol as it is developed.

Much of the impetus for compiling physician practice data bases and developing physician profile information comes from the business community, which continues to search for ways to control the cost of paying for their employees' health care. Companies, either working together or individually, contract with organizations that collect such data from hospitals and develop benchmarks against which hospital cost and outcome information can be compared. Hospitals and their physician staffs use this information to try to lower costs because they know that companies are beginning to choose providers based on which ones the data show to be the most efficient.

Physician Response to Economic Credentialing

Some state medical associations, as well as the American Medical Association, have developed position papers expressing distrust of economic credentialing. For example, according to the Medical Society of the State of New York:

> Some hospitals have adopted the stance that their ability to control the medical staff is critical to their goal of generating broader operations bases, and increasing profit margins. In addition, there appears to be a recognition that certain medical specialists can generate considerable profits for the institution. On the other hand, a physician with the "wrong" mix of patients (usually very sick and underinsured) can have a negative impact on the hospital's bottom line. Based on these economic considerations, hospitals may attempt to determine which physicians can use the hospital, how care is delivered, how much care is provided, and what type of patients will be admitted to the hospital.[1]

The paper goes on to warn that it is "the medical staff's responsibility for ensuring that economic considerations do not override quality considerations in providing patient care."[2]

After examining information prepared by the California Medical Association regarding the kinds of data available for use in credentialing, the Medical Society of New

York added its own categories of hospital-collected data and grouped the categories to show which ones it believes are valid for quality assurance purposes, which ones *may* be valid for quality assurance purposes, and which ones have no quality assurance value. Included in the list of criteria that may affect quality and thus may be valid in credentialing are things such as length of stay, comparison of resources used, and comparative profiles of physician outcomes and resources utilized within the same DRG. On the list of criteria that do not apply to quality and should not be used are revenue per physician, resource utilization in dollars, charges comparison, physician profit by cost, admission rates, and number of hospital-owned outpatient services utilized.[3]

There are at least two barriers to hospitals that use physician cost profiles in the credentialing process. The first is physician resistance to the imposition of what is seen by the physicians as a hospital plan to increase profits without regard to quality of care. If economic credentialing is perceived to be purely financial without consideration of quality, physicians will resist. Clearly, the hospitals that will be most successful in incorporating economic data into credentialing will be those that use the information as an educational tool to demonstrate to physicians that they can provide the same quality of care at a lower cost. Further, if economic data are integrated with quality assurance information before they are used to affect physicians' practices, physicians will find economic credentialing efforts easier to support.

The second barrier is that the data cannot yet be formulated precisely enough to exclude a physician from membership or limit privileges without legal challenge. Particularly in facilities where patients are seen by several specialists, the cost of a patient's care cannot be attributed to the particular physician who may have ordered the tests and procedures. The best the hospital can do is to make an assumption about which physician to attribute the stay to, usually the physician who either admitted, discharged, or attended the patient. The physician profile of that patient's stay will belong to that physician, regardless of who actually ordered the extra tests or unnecessarily lengthened the patient's stay. Until the data-gathering process becomes more reliable, physician profiles are better used to persuade than to exclude.

The Legal Basis of Economic Credentialing

The issue of economic credentialing is new enough that challenges have not yet proceeded through the courts to final decisions; however, there is case law to support a hospital's ability to tie physicians' privileges to their economic impact on the institution. To be successful in defending economic credentialing, the hospital must be able to show that the criteria it uses to evaluate physicians are rationally based on a legitimate interest of the hospital. Clearly, a hospital could take action against a physician who consistently ordered tests that were either inappropriate for the patient's condition or redundant. The basis for the action is that excessive and unnecessary testing is not patient care of the quality the hospital provides. Although the issue is one of quality, it also is one of cost, for both the patient and the hospital.

A further refinement of the same example is the instance in which a medical service of the hospital develops treatment protocols for particular medical conditions, based on recommendations from the medical specialty society. Tests and procedures are scheduled at optimum points in the patient's stay, thus reducing cost, eliminating unnecessary testing, and reducing the patient's length of stay. The department's utilization review committee would be justified in seeking an explanation from a physician whose treatment of patients with such conditions consistently fell outside the protocol. The physician's patients may be sicker or have more complications than other physicians' patients. However, if the physician cannot provide an explanation that is medically acceptable and the bylaws call for reporting the information at the time of reappointment, the credentials committee could evaluate the physician's practice and make a recommendation based on the information available from both the department and the physician being evaluated. If the credentials committee believes that the physician is unnecessarily overutilizing hospital resources, it may want to recommend additional education, a shorter appointment period, or a probationary period within which to evaluate whether the physician is able to bring utilization within the approved protocols. If the physician cannot then conform to the recommended protocol for the cases that fit it, the hospital may alter the physician's privileges. This action is legally defensible as long as the criteria by which the physician is measured are objective and applied fairly to all and as long as the hospital follows a procedure previously set out in the bylaws for taking such action.

All actions taken by a hospital based on economic criteria may not be so easily defended. A hospital probably could not require, without overriding justification, that, as a condition of staff membership, the physician agree to refer patients only to hospital-owned subsidiaries for outpatient services or that the physician agree not to be a member of the medical staff of competing hospitals.[4] Some authors have suggested that requiring a physician to admit a minimum number of patients each year in order to be a member of the staff may be an illegal inducement for patient referrals that violates the Medicare fraud and abuse statutes.[5] Applying criteria to terminate or reduce a physician's privileges that describe only the profit or cost a physician adds to the hospital's financial position, without considering quality or intensity of illness, also may be difficult. Using credentialing criteria where economic factors are an integral part of the quality of the patient's care—such as requiring efficient scheduling of tests, eliminating duplicative or unnecessary tests, and reducing length of stay—are the most easily justified and defended.

Traditional Forms of Economic Credentialing

There are two traditional forms of economic credentialing: the exclusive contract and the medical staff development plan.

Exclusive Contract

Contracts between hospitals and physician groups under which the physicians are the exclusive provider of a medical service are used by hospitals to control quality of care, ensure physician coverage at critical times, provide care to indigent patients, foster a close working relationship between the physicians and other physicians and staff, and have some control over cost. These are legitimate policy reasons recognized by the legal system for hospitals to enter into exclusive contracts. The hospital should articulate the reasons for the exclusive arrangement in the contract, in minutes of meetings of the governing board, and in hospital policies.

These contracts have long been used by hospitals for emergency, radiology, and pathology services. Hospitals are just beginning to use exclusive contracts for other physician specialty services, such as cardiology, where the cost of procedures is high and quality is critical to the patient's survival. Court case after court case has upheld the use of exclusive contracts, many of the decisions citing their "economic efficiencies."[6] In those recent cases where excluded physicians successfully challenged exclusive contracts, the physician prevailed because the hospital had violated either the provisions of the contract or the medical staff bylaws in implementing the contract.[7]

One of the hospital's challenges when it implements an exclusive contract is determining how to terminate the privileges of other physicians who practice that specialty. If the exclusive group is replacing a group whose contract says specifically that the physicians' privileges terminate when the contract terminates and terminate without a due process hearing, the physicians will be bound by the terms of the contract.

However, if such a provision is not in the contract, or if the hospital is replacing a service that has been open, the hospital will have to be more careful in terminating physician privileges.

Courts have, however, upheld the hospital's ability to restrict its medical staff.[8] The hospital must show a solid, well-documented business reason for the change, the change must be implemented by the governing board, and the physicians involved should be given a hearing. If a hospital follows these steps, the court probably will not interfere with what it perceives to be a legitimate business purpose. Physicians challenge exclusive contracts by alleging that the contracts prevent competition. However, courts find that a hospital that has an exclusive contract with a physician group becomes more competitive. As long as the hospital follows its own policies and those policies are fair, hospitals can use exclusive contracts as a tool to manage costs.

Medical Staff Development Plans

Another economic tool the hospital may use is a medical staff development plan. Implementing a development plan presents more legal difficulties than implementing exclusive contracts, but is manageable if done properly. Using demographic data from the hospital's service area, the hospital develops a plan describing the medical service it will offer that meets the health care needs of the community, that specifies the equipment and staff resources required, and that states the number of specialty physicians required to provide the service. The governing board adopts the plan as a tool to facilitate the efficient use of resources. If the medical staff develops the plan, it will be viewed as an attempt to limit competition. If the hospital's governing board adopts it, limiting the number of doctors probably is not anticompetitive.

When the plan is implemented, the hospital accepts applications only from physicians in those specialties that have not reached the maximum number specified in the plan. Applications from physicians in specialties that are not accepting applications are filed and considered in the order received at the time that there is a vacancy in that specialty. All applications are considered based on the criteria approved by the board. Applications from physicians who are members of specialty groups that already have privileges at the hospital are not given priority, but are considered after all the applications received before them have been reviewed and acted on.

The key to defending a legal challenge by a physician who sues for being excluded from the staff as a result of a medical staff development plan is to show that:

1. The plan is based on objective data.
2. It meets the needs of the community.
3. It was developed by the board and not the physicians.
4. It is implemented fairly.
5. It treats all physicians alike, with no preferences given to any specialty group or individual.

Defending legal challenges to closing one or more services of the medical staff is difficult. The hospital's attorneys should be involved in the planning stages of a medical staff development plan.

The Future of Economic Credentialing

The forces demanding change in the current health delivery system and a reduction in the escalating costs are pushing hospitals and physician groups closer together. Some observers believe that the traditional medical staff will be replaced by one or more multispecialty groups. The American Hospital Association, although not advocating exclusive contracts between hospitals and physicians, suggests that providers of health care create integrated health care systems through contracts that hospitals would have with primary care physicians, nursing homes, home health agencies, and hospitals offering specialty services, so that providers are better able to manage overall cost and the use of services by enrollees.[9] Others suggest that, rather than reimbursing physicians and hospitals separately for their services, both be reimbursed by a single fee, called a *global fee* that would be paid to the hospital and then divided between the physician and hospital in whatever way the two negotiate. If global fees are part of health care reform, hospitals will have no choice but to allow only the most cost-efficient physicians to practice in the facility, whether as a part of a traditional medical staff, as a part of a contracted physician group, or as an employee of the hospital.

Even as politicians make speeches about revolutionizing the health care delivery system, providers themselves are making painful, gradual changes to reduce the cost of health care delivery. One important change is to require physicians to use fewer tests and perform them at key times during the patient's stay; to think about cost and to factor cost into health care decisions about supplies, equipment, tests, and procedures; and, most of all to share information with each other to develop clinical pathways rather than work in isolation. The courts will allow hospitals to govern themselves without interference as long as they follow the simple guidelines that have been set forth: that (1) the board set reasonable criteria for decisions based on well-documented need, (2) the criteria be in writing and communicated, (3) the criteria be applied objectively to all, and (4) physicians who are adversely affected be given the right to be heard by an objective decision maker.

Emerging Issues and Trends

As the practical impact of the National Practitioner Data Bank, antidumping laws, and other laws unfold, new issues are likely to emerge that will affect medical staff privileging. The same can be said of nonlegal initiatives, such as the shift to quality improvement and greater reliance on noninstitutional forms of health care delivery.

From a practical standpoint, health care facilities should not view the medical staff credentialing and privileging process as a static concept. Like other areas of day-to-day management, credentialing and privileging procedures should be reviewed periodically with a critical eye toward the changing environment. At the same time, those involved in the process should remain current on key issues that may have a direct impact on their work.

Two recent issues typify this concern. One involves the hospital's response when notified that the physician insurer ceases to operate. The other involves management of a staff physician with AIDS. As each example illustrates, these are "hot" topics that require a consultative approach among those responsible for medical staff credentialing, the board, senior management, legal counsel, and the risk manager.

When the Physician Insurer Ceases to Operate

Most hospitals require physicians to provide documentary proof that they have a specified amount of malpractice insurance coverage. This requirement is found in hospital bylaws governing the medical staff.

What happens when the physician insurer goes bankrupt or is ordered by a state insurance commission to cease operation? Does this mean that the staff physicians insured by these groups should be prevented from performing surgery? From performing invasive diagnostic tests? From admitting or treating patients?

Technically speaking, physicians caught in this situation are in violation of those bylaws that require proof of ongoing malpractice insurance coverage as a condition for holding staff privileges. Although insurance can often be found for these physicians in only a matter of days, surgical or invasive test misadventures can occur at any time, including during the brief interlude in which the search is on for an alternate physicians' liability carrier.

Temporary suspension of physicians caught in this trap has definite implications. For example, the hospital faces the prospect of significant loss of revenue. The situation may play havoc with operating room schedules, day surgery departments, and diagnostic centers. Additionally, discord between the physicians affected and the hospital usually can be anticipated.

Some hospitals may take the position that if the risk exposure is only going to be a "matter of days," they will leave well enough alone. However, in doing so, they may not be giving sufficient thought to corporate fiscal integrity. Moreover, the staff physicians who do have appropriate coverage may become disgruntled, claiming that the hospital is "playing favorites" with those caught in the insurance bind.

Giving thoughtful consideration to both sides, the hospital has to make a decision. The situation calls for prompt action, complete with an analysis of the likely risk exposure, the availability of other insurance options, and the financial impact of temporarily suspending the privileges of physicians affected by the sudden absence of insurance. Continuity of care for patients in the hospital and those scheduled for investigatory or corrective procedures also must be factored into the decision-making process.

The decision makers include the board, senior managers, and the risk manager acting on the advice of legal counsel. The bottom line is that the choice made must be in the best interests of the hospital and its patients. The board must decide what choice best reflects its stated mission or purpose and protects the hospital's corporate integrity. In many cases, this may result in the board's decision to suspend staff privileges temporarily, pending documented proof of required liability coverage.

When a Staff Physician Has AIDS

Another emerging issue in recent years that is likely to have an impact on the credentialing process involves HIV-infected physicians. As the following case illustrates, an action to revoke privileges on the basis of HIV status can lead to charges of discrimination by the physician affected by the decision.

In a well-publicized case in New Jersey,[10] a hospital moved to withdraw staff privileges from a staff physician who had AIDS. The physician, an ear, nose, and throat specialist, had sought medical treatment at the hospital. In the course of the medical workup, he tested positive for HIV. A glaring breach of confidentiality occurred and the hospital board learned of the physician's health status.

The physician did not take lightly the idea that his staff privileges should be revoked on the basis of his HIV status. Thereafter, having taken into account the impact of state laws prohibiting discrimination, the health facility took a different tact. It adopted a requirement that, as a condition of staff privileges, HIV-infected physicians must disclose their status to patients as part of the consent process.

The physician filed a lawsuit for breach of confidentiality. He included an allegation that the hospital had unlawfully discriminated against him by requiring him to inform his patients of his HIV status as a requirement of staff privileges. The New Jersey Superior Court ruled that hospitals can add conditions to the privileges granted to staff physicians, including in this case a special consent requirement. The court took the position that a surgeon should reveal his physical condition to patients because it was a risk of the surgery itself. Although the risk was characterized as remote, the chance of HIV transmission from a surgeon to patient during an operation was considered a material piece of information requiring disclosure under the law governing informed consent.

Some might argue that the hospital "panicked" in this case and did not think through all the consequences of revoking the physician's privileges. Others might claim that in the end the hospital took appropriate action. If the HIV-infected physician had been a psychiatrist, for example, rather than someone who performs invasive procedures, the outcome could have been much different. However, the key point to be made by this illustration is that hospitals must be on top of such emerging trends or issues and must be prepared to take action.

Conclusion

In an effort to control the escalating cost of care provided by physicians using their facilities, many hospitals are beginning to incorporate utilization information into their credentialing process. This concept, called economic credentialing, is intended to encourage physicians to manage their practices more efficiently by making economic data a measure of performance. Although there is physician resistance to the concept, there is sufficient case law to support the hospital's position on economic credentialing provided that the hospital can demonstrate that it is a legitimate criterion for maintaining the quality of care delivery.

The economics of health care is just one issue having an impact on the credentialing process. Hospitals must periodically review their credentialing process with an eye toward not only improving it, but also enabling it to respond to every emerging issue and trend that may ultimately affect the standards and quality of the care delivered.

Notes and References

1. *Economic Credentialing and Exclusive Contracts: MSSNY Policy Paper*, p. 1.

2. MSSNY Policy Paper.

3. MSSNY Policy Paper, Appendix A.

4. Note that the Florida Circuit Court upheld a hospital's right to deny staff membership to a physician on the basis that he was the chair of the heart surgery department at a competing hospital. Rosenblum v. Tallahassee Memorial Regional Medical Center, Inc., No. 91-589 (Fla. Cir. Ct. June, 1992).

5. Benesch, K. Economic credentialing and the fraud and abuse caveat. *The Medical Staff Counselor* 6(4):27-35, Fall 1992.

6. Baxter, M. Exclusive contracting: the original economic credentialing. *Journal of Health and Hospital Law* 26(4):97-103, Apr. 1993.

7. Baxter, p. 99.

8. Robinson v. Magovern, 521 F.Supp 842, *aff'd mem.*, 688 F.2d 824 3rd Cir. (1982), *cert. denied* 459 U.S. 971 (1982).

9. *National Health Care Reform: Refining and Advancing the Vision*, adopted by the AHA Board of Trustees in May 1992.

10. Estate of Behringer v. The Medical Center at Princeton, 249 N.J. Super 597, 592 A2d 1251 (NJ Sup. 1991).

9 Credentialing Issues for Small and Rural Hospitals

Introduction

There are few basic differences between a small hospital and a large hospital or between a rural hospital and an urban hospital. Their basic structure is the same, as is their organization except perhaps that the medical staff may not be departmentalized in a smaller facility. Modifications are made solely on account of size, differences in services offered, and the role played by each hospital in its community. It is these modifications that affect the interpersonal relations among the hospital's physicians, board members, and others, and thus its system of credentialing.

With these differences in mind, this chapter focuses on the credentialing challenges that face small and rural hospitals. It also examines the option of regional credentialing and the issue of handling community and media pressures.

The Challenges Facing Small and Rural Hospitals

Small and rural hospitals are particularly susceptible to challenges on four different issues. These include interpersonal relations between individuals within the hospital and with the community, business relations between individuals within the hospital and with the community, the lack of medical manpower, and the potential for conflict of interest and collusion.

Interpersonal Relations

Of all the challenges that affect interpersonal relations in a small or rural hospital, that of medical staff credentialing often is the most difficult. The credentialing process brings together colleagues who work in a situation in which they are asked to judge each other and to make decisions that may affect their livelihood and perhaps their entire careers. It places physicians who ordinarily are on an equal footing socially and professionally in the unequal relationship of judge and judged. In a closely-knit community where the number of physicians is small, these factors take on increased importance.

This challenge also affects members of the board of trustees who are not used to judging their social equals. As sometime patients, they also are not used to judging physicians, because the traditional relationship between a physician and patient has not always been one of equality. This can put trustees in a very difficult position.

In large urban hospitals, these problems often are not as acute. Physicians and trustees may not always know each other on a personal basis. They may live in different neighborhoods and have little or no social contact outside the hospital. This minimal personal interaction makes it easier for all concerned to concentrate on their roles as committee or board members without the psychological pressure that is ordinarily present when all concerned are part of a close-knit community.

Additionally, hospitals (and those associated with them) in small communities, and even in ethnic, religious, and other close-knit communities within urban areas, are more likely to be subject to the pressures and influences exerted from outside the hospital whether by residents, organizations, businesses, or the press. For example, a community newspaper can have much more influence over issues affecting the hospital in a small community than a high-circulation daily will over a hospital in a metropolitan area.

However, it should be noted that despite the fact that the mass media is centered in urban areas, small communities are not immune from their attention. Because of the national and international structure of the mass media, small and rural hospitals must be aware of potential press interest in their activities. Because press coverage can have a far greater effect on a small community than it would have on a large city, this awareness carries a special importance.

Business Relations

Another factor that is more likely to be pertinent in small and rural communities is that members of the medical staff and trustees may have business relations with each other quite apart from the practice of medicine. Members of the hospital's medical staff also may be partners in the same practice and yet be required to judge each other's conduct apart from that relationship. Thus, any decision made regarding medical staff privileges can have a serious impact on that group practice. Although such situations also may occur in large institutions and communities, their occurrence is less likely given the larger numbers of people involved.

This relationship can be the basis of a dilemma in taking corrective action against physicians in small and rural hospitals. Portions of the Health Care Quality Improvement Act grant the hospital immunity from liability only if it follows the minimum due process requirements stated in the act. Because one of these requirements is that competitors of the affected practitioner may not participate in any decision-making process that may result in the revocation, suspension, or restriction of privileges, the rural hospital is faced with the problem of being able to find practitioners who are not in a competitive position.

Lack of Medical Manpower

Another problem affecting medical staff credentialing in small and rural communities is the concern for increased medical manpower. In large cities, because of the greater availability of physicians and physicians in particular specialties, decisions on granting privileges can be based more easily on factors other than community need. Because small communities traditionally have had trouble attracting physicians, the need to ensure medical manpower can frequently have a greater influence on the credentialing decision than the quality of service that the physician is able to offer.

However, despite the influence of this concern, it is hoped that small and rural hospital boards will make decisions with respect to the credentialing of physicians in a manner that is unbiased, fair, and in accordance with the goals and mission of the hospital. No other consideration should affect their decision-making process.

Members of committees may not be bound in the same way as trustees. They must therefore be instructed to advise the board on the effects that credentialing decisions would have on the standards of care offered by the hospital. In turn, the board should instruct those committees on what criteria they are to apply in making their recommendations. In this way, the trustees clearly understand the basis of the recommendations and can judge them accordingly.

Conflict of Interest and Collusion

One situation to be avoided is that of conflict of interest or even collusion. This means that no one making a privileges determination should have any personal interest in the decision, nor should any personal arrangements be made to affect the outcome. Even in the event that collusion results in a decision that is beneficial for the hospital and the community it serves, given the negative perception that this practice invokes, it should be avoided. There should not even be a suspicion of collusion.

Ethically speaking, no person involved in the credentialing process or in the determination of medical staff privileges should have a contract or proposed contract with a physician whose privileges are being considered. There should be no appearance that anyone in such a position would benefit personally by the granting, restriction, or removal of a physician's privileges. For example, a physician whose practice may be diminished by the introduction of another physician into the community or whose access to beds may be decreased by the introduction of another physician would be placed in such a conflict of interest. A trustee would be placed in a similar position if the incoming physician made an offer to buy property or to lease office space owned by that trustee. Although undoubtedly some physicians or trustees as members of the community at large may benefit by that decision, no one should derive a unique personal benefit that would not be available to the rest of the community.

A straightforward way to eliminate this problem is for any board or committee member faced with such a conflict to resign. However, this solution is not always practical, especially in small communities, because the number of people willing to serve in these capacities often is so limited that, over time, hospitals would run short of volunteers.

There is a simple compromise. Any member of a committee or board who is faced with a decision regarding a physician's privileges should examine whether he or she has a personal interest in that physician. This interest may be a close friendship, a family relationship, a business relationship, or a social relationship, such as when both are on the board of the local golf club. If that member feels that a personal interest exists, he or she should make it known to the other board or committee members before any discussion takes place.

This admission should be recorded in the minutes and the member should leave the meeting before discussion of the physician's case begins. The member's absence should be noted. At no time should he or she take any public position or make any comment on either the physician or any evidence that is or might come before the board or committee. After the discussion is over and a decision is made, the member may return to the meeting. This fact should also be recorded. Given the social structure of small towns, it is often very difficult not to make some passing remark because of the frequent informal meetings that take place, particularly in public places.

Despite these efforts, accusations of conflict of interest will be heard. To assist the member and to maintain the reputation of the institution as well as the individuals involved, the institution should adopt a policy on conflict of interest. This policy should be well publicized to all incumbent and future medical staff members, as well as to all board members, all employees, and the local media. When a privileges decision is made, the process should be carefully reviewed to ensure that there has been no conflict of interest and that one will not surface in the future. It is important to remember that the appearance of collusion can be just as damaging as actual collusion.

Regional Credentialing

The most difficult aspect of the credentialing process in small and rural institutions is that a small group of people comprising a high proportion of the staff (in some cases the entire medical staff) is being asked to make a judgment on themselves. There is always the inherent threat that if the members of the assessing body take a negative view of one of their own members, there may be a tendency toward retaliation. In any case, it certainly will not engender good relations among medical staff members.

One solution to this problem is to assess medical staff qualifications and performance on a regional basis by bringing together the credentialing processes of a number of hospitals within a specific geographic area. This collaboration could include all the institutions in the region or only those that are similar. This and similar solutions are being used in parts of Canada. To apply them to the United States may raise some antitrust considerations, although these may be less significant under the impending health care reform. To minimize antitrust issues, great care must be taken to avoid allocating services or equipment among participating hospitals.

A number of alternative approaches also may be taken. The most sweeping would be to establish one medical staff for a number of small hospitals. Privileges may be given for all institutions or for some. In certain respects, this would be no different from the present arrangement in which many physicians hold privileges in more than one hospital. The extent of those privileges is not necessarily the same in all the institutions.

Usually, the physician applies to each hospital separately and each hospital conducts its own credentialing process. Under a combined approach, the physician would submit one application requesting privileges at all or some of the area hospitals. For example, he or she may request obstetrical privileges in three institutions and surgical privileges in only one.

The problem with such an approach is that it is difficult to coordinate. Credentialing should be handled through one central point, and review of the application and current performance also would have to be centralized. The danger is that those who are conducting a credentials review may be affected by parochial interests and needs rather those of the individual institutions and the communities they serve.

Decision making would still be done at the individual board level. Great care must be taken to avoid "horse-trading" in making recommendations so that the board can feel assured that its interests are not subjugated to those of other institutions in the region. This would be particularly important if the decisions regarding privileges were to be made by a regional body outside the individual board.

A compromise that would minimize the risk of parochial politics interfering with the credentialing process would be to maintain the credentialing authority, and even a certain amount of the review and recommendation process, at the individual board level and have it supplemented by a joint regional review body. The benefit to this approach is that a joint regional review body would be in a better position to take into account the needs of each institution and those of the region as a whole.

Using Objective Criteria

The regional credentials committee would use objective criteria established by each institution with input from the regional body and any outside experts that may be brought in from time to time. The process may be enhanced through formal relationships with other institutions where the same or related privileges are granted. The limited statistical information available from small facilities would be pooled and stratified to present an accurate picture of physician performance and treatment outcomes compared to those of peers. A few anomalies found in the case of a physician's hospital practice would not be given undue consideration.

One hurdle to overcome is the attitude that every rural hospital can provide any service that an individual physician or surgeon is capable of carrying out. Any credentialing process must take into account the ability not only of the physician, but also of the hospital in terms of the staff, equipment, and finances needed by its medical staff to carry out their privileges at an appropriate standard.

A regional committee needs each participating hospital to supply objective criteria for guidance on what each particular hospital has decided it can and cannot do. The committee must be regularly informed of any changes in equipment, staff, or practice patterns, because such changes may occasionally necessitate changes in privileges.

However, special care must be taken in changing a physician's privileges on the basis of the hospital's existing resources so as not to trigger a report on physician performance to the National Practitioner Data Bank. A decision to alter privileges may be perceived as a reflection on the physician's clinical competence when, in fact, the decision is being made on the basis of the hospital's inability to support the carrying out of those privileges.

A regional committee is more likely to have the resources and expertise to make decisions on granting or changing privileges based on physician's performance. This committee is in a better position to know that if a physician does not perform a specific number of procedures of a certain type or complexity to remain clinically competent, his or her privileges to do those procedures should be withheld.

It frequently is easier for a regional committee to make such recommendations because it is not personally involved with the physician who will be affected by the decision. However, the committee can only make its recommendations if it receives regular reports from the hospitals on a continuing basis. These reports should not be sent only on request because a recommendation may be necessary on its own initiative apart from actual applications for privileges or renewals.

The guidelines necessary to make recommendations should be established by the committee and submitted to the board of trustees of the institution it is serving. The committee should not wait for the hospital's board to set up such guidelines, because boards generally do not have the expertise to do so. However, the board of each hospital must make a determination as to what services it is able and wishes to provide.

Private hospital consulting firms also are available to assist in the credentialing process. Such firms often are able to bring a great deal of experience to the decision-making process that may not be available to a small hospital committee. However, it is important to ensure that such firms have a specific understanding of small and rural hospitals and can apply appropriate information to those settings.

Taking Precautions

In the establishment of regional committees for the credentialing process, precautions (as previously noted) must be taken to avoid antitrust prosecution. The danger is that a regional grouping may attempt to divide up the market in order to avoid medical staff disputes and thus make credentialing decisions on the basis of this division, rather than on the physician's abilities and the appropriateness of the requested privileges being given at a particular hospital. This situation may alter under health care reform.

One further caution should be noted. Regional committees should take special care to review and comply with state statutes protecting confidentiality of the quality assurance and utilization review data that may be submitted by individual hospitals.

Community and Media Pressure

Every institution, whether located in a small town or a large metropolitan area, is subject to community and media pressure. Even though such pressure may come from only a small segment of the community, it can nevertheless be just as effective. In metropolitan areas, members of the community are less dependent on a particular hospital for services and generally have more divergent interests, whereas in small towns, the hospital is one of the few major institutions that has an impact on the life of the community. Along with the municipal council, the school board, and the church, little else is controlled from within the community. The result is that the affairs of the hospital become the affairs of each of the community's residents.

Public feeling tends to be more widespread and much of it is voiced by word of mouth rather than through the media. Depending on the nature of the community, information and opinion also tend to spread more quickly than they do in large cities. Conversations in front of the local grocery store or at a service club meeting are soon spread throughout the entire community. Because board members, hospital employees, and practitioners usually have closer and more frequent social relationships with each other, discussions of hospital affairs tend to be repeated by outsiders to those who are immediately associated with the hospital.

Community and media pressure invariably arises during a crisis. When medical staff privileges are involved, the crisis usually occurs when a physician either publicly complains of being refused privileges or has been removed from the medical staff.

In any such instance, there will be many patients, frequently with the sympathy of their family and friends, who have been satisfied with the physician's services. Because of action being taken against the physician, these patients will lose the services he or she provided. They may even lose the physician who will not be able to practice in the community without hospital privileges, or without the privileges desired, and who may prefer to no longer work in the community on that basis.

At the same time, many in the community will support the board and the actions of the hospital. Many of these positions are highly emotional and are based on rumor and innuendo. Because the story in the press (if it reaches the press) often has the potential to encourage rumors by what is not said rather than by what is, people can always find fuel to support whatever position they wish to take on the controversy.

The effect of such a controversy can be devastating to both the hospital and its staff. It can hurt any public financial campaigns for many years to come, as potential donors seek to "get even" with the hospital. Many potential donors will be reluctant to contribute because of their decreased confidence in the institution in allowing such a controversy to take place, perceiving the issue to be a sign of the hospital's weakness and disorganization. Many may even transfer their charitable allegiance to larger institutions in a neighboring community, thus overcoming any loyalty they may owe to their community and its hospital. To lessen the risk of medical staff controversy, the board of any small or rural hospital must be alert to potential problems and should be ready to respond to such challenges.

Such controversies usually arise because of the community's lack of understanding of what credentialing is all about. Thus, to anticipate their eventuality, boards of small hospitals should undertake community education campaigns on a regular basis, and they should do so with as much support from the medical staff as possible. Physicians should realize that public understanding of the credentialing system is as beneficial to them as it is to the hospital, because any public controversy over privileges can have a very detrimental effect on them as members of the medical staff and as committee members involved in making the decision. It can adversely affect their relations with their patients and certainly with their colleagues.

The message that must be brought to the attention of the public should clarify a number of credentialing issues. These include:

1. The fact that a physician has a license to practice medicine does not give him or her the legal right to treat patients within a hospital and to use the beds, facilities, and supplies of that hospital.
2. The hospital has a duty to both its patients and the community at large to provide services according to reasonable standards of care and to provide support for the medical care given by physicians in the hospital. Further, physicians cannot practice medicine in a hospital without the support of nurses, technologists, allied health professionals, and equipment and supplies. Similarly,

physicians must maintain clinical proficiency in order to be able to perform specific procedures in the facility.

3. Every hospital must decide what sort of services it has the resources to provide. Although it would certainly be more convenient for the hospital to be able to provide every conceivable type of care within the community, this may not be possible because of the lack of expertise, personnel, and equipment.

4. Many of the services that were once provided by the community hospital can no longer be provided because to do so would be to provide them at a lower standard than is currently acceptable. In many instances, the standard of care in providing a service is the same, but involves greater risks of something going wrong that could be avoided if the patient were sent to a larger hospital. In the past, such risks may have been accepted because the hospital had no choice. Today, that is no longer the case.

5. The fact that many excellent physicians provide high-quality service in their private offices does not mean that they can practice medicine at the hospital at the same level. There are physicians who have worked at some of the most famous teaching hospitals in the world who are not suitable to practice in small hospitals where the resources to perform the same or similar work are not available. Thus, the fact that it is inappropriate for that physician to be carrying out certain procedures in a small hospital is not always a reflection on his or her competence.

6. The board of trustees governs the hospital in the interests of the community, but is not expert in the technical and professional aspects of hospital or medical management. For this reason, to determine whether a particular physician should or should not be carrying out certain or any procedures in the hospital, the board must rely on the expert advice of those who are qualified, just as private citizens must rely on the expert advice of physicians, lawyers, dentists, plumbers, and accountants. When that expertise is not available on a regular basis, it may be necessary to establish a regional review committee to bring together this expertise. Another reason for setting up such a committee is to relieve local physicians of the burden of having to judge colleagues.

7. To make certain that everyone is treated fairly and in the same manner, the board has adopted a set of objective criteria on which advice is given and decisions are made. In this way, the board is not asked to make a judgment on matters that are outside its expertise but, rather, can base a review of the physician on these criteria.

8. Physicians will be given every opportunity permitted by law to present as much information as possible regarding their performance and the established standards.

A document of this type may make it easier for committee and board members to state clearly and objectively that the physician either did or did not meet the requirements. Additionally, it will place the community on notice that as long as the board and its committees have themselves followed the rules, they cannot be subject to personal pressure.

This information should be as widely disseminated as possible. Taking this action will undoubtedly be far less expensive and disruptive than a medical staff dispute with misdirected community pressure being brought to bear on committee and board members.

Conclusion

Although all hospitals, large and small, face many of the same problems in credentialing physicians, small and rural hospitals are more acutely challenged in their efforts

to manage the credentialing process. Because physicians and hospital board members in small communities are more likely to have closer and more frequent personal relationships, including outside business relationships, than their urban counterparts, they are subject to greater psychological and community pressures when they must sit in judgment of one another's work and conduct.

One way to ease their burden is to establish a regional review or advisory committee that would oversee the credentialing process for physicians seeking privileges at hospitals within a specific geographic region, using objective criteria provided by the hospitals involved. In addition to each hospital's standards of care, these criteria are based on the institution's ability to supply the resources required to carry out certain privileges. Each institution maintains its own autonomy, decides what services it will offer to the community, and makes its own decisions about what equipment and support staff will be available.

A further benefit to setting objective criteria for the credentialing process is that they can be used to help stem public controversy that can arise when a popular physician's privileges are restricted or revoked. Thus, hospital boards should work with their medical staffs to educate the community on what these criteria are, why they are important, and how they are applied in the process. The education effort should make it clear that privileges sometimes are restricted or denied for reasons that have nothing to do with a physician's competence but, rather, may have to do with the hospital's lack of resources to carry out the privileges being requested.

Additional Books of Interest

Physician Recruitment and Retention: Practical Techniques for Exceptional Results

by Roger G. Bonds and Kimberly A. Pulliam

A comprehensive, how-to guide for planning and implementing physician recruitment programs in health care organizations. The first half of the book provides a framework, or understanding, of the overall planning process and what will be needed before a successful plan can be implemented. The second half deals with implementation. This practical, easy-to-understand guide shows how to establish an effective, cost-efficient physician recruitment program from start-up to contract negotiation.

1991. 219 pages, 28 figures, 1 table.
Catalog No. E99-145158
$45.00 (AHA members, $35.00)

Medical Staff Peer Review: A Strategy for Motivation and Performance

by Daniel A. Lang, M.D.

"An excellent book of major importance to chiefs of staff and V-P's of medical affairs, to CEO's and boards, and to hospital staff working in support of medical quality assurance."
   Leadership in Health Services

The text provides strategies for making the medical staff peer review process work effectively and efficiently and for eliciting renewed commitment and full participation. Chapters discuss the processes of direct peer review, patient care screens, exception analysis, and performance data analysis, as well as approaches to corrective actions, legal issues, motivation, and responses to such emerging environmental changes as external peer review. Includes a self-assessment tool to help institutions evaluate peer review readiness and performance.

1991. 145 pages, 30 figures, 2 tables.
Catalog No. E99-145157
$42.50 (AHA members, $34.00)

To order, call TOLL FREE
1-800-AHA-2626